A Glass Act

David Pilkington

St Helens, where the sparrows wake up coughing ...

Ken Dodd

"He's utterly convinced that he's being exiled to St. **Helen's**, poor devil!"

A Glass Act

David Pilkington

Published by David Pilkington

© The author 2010

ISBN 0 9567302 0 6

Printed by Tyneside Free Press
Charlotte Square
Newcastle upon Tyne NE1 4XF

To my family:

Yvonne,
Simon, Martin, Julia, Lucy, Edward

Contents

List of Figures

List of Plates

Acknowledgements

To Yvonne, my wife, extra-special thanks are due, for support and patience in putting up with a distracted and sometimes absent husband during the writing of this book.

I would also like to thank many friends who have helped me: Michael Ayton, my editor, who knocked it into shape; Irene Dixon, my secretary, who faithfully deciphered my handwriting and produced the basic text; Peter Snowdon, my illustrator, whose visual effects lift and enliven the whole work; Richard Bolton, my researcher who worked on the non-glassmaking aspects of the story; the late Theo Barker, official company historian whose bible *The Glassmakers*, along with other books of his, have been the foundation structure on which this work is based; Elizabeth Williams-Ellis (Fellow of the Society of Antiquaries and my cousin), whose book *The Pilkington Story* has been an important scholarly source of family history; Dr David Bricknell, whose book *Float*, describing the licensing of float worldwide, is another authoritative source; and Ron Taylor, who worked on the chemistry of float.

Other names too stand out in my mind: Jennifer Jones, Sir Harry Pilkington's daughter; Rosalind Christian, Sir Alastair Pilkington's daughter; Elisabeth Ratiu, my sister; Isabel Henniger, my cousin; Sol Kay; John Gillespie; Les Bot; George Gaskell; and hundreds of friends and colleagues at all levels in the company, interacting with whom has made my life so fulfilling.

Finally, I would like to record my debt to the late Tom Grundy, whose book *The Global Miracle of Float* is an impressive 'worm's eye' view of what it was like to struggle and sweat and risk injury actually making the glass. To all those who did so struggle this book is also gratefully dedicated.

Introduction

This is the story of 170 years and five generations of commitment by the Pilkington family to the mysterious stuff called glass, as told by a member of the fourth generation. This 'glass' was 'flat glass' for windows and mirrors.

The summary of the commitment of the Pilkingtons to glass is straightforward:

- The first generation pioneered and established it.

- The second generation consolidated it.

- The third generation nearly lost it.

- The fourth generation sold their birthright after a golden age.

- The fifth generation mounted a rearguard action. They couldn't hold on to what had been lost.

The structure of this document will follow the above historical form, but there will be an overarching division into two parts:

Part One.   The historical part, already researched fully and written about by others, Theo Barker and Elizabeth Williams-Ellis.

Part Two.   The modern part, where I am on stage.

The story of this dance between the Pilkingtons and glass is extraordinary by any standards, but the climax of float in the fourth generation makes it a story that must be told. It may be hard for those outside the flat glass industry to visualise how great was the impact of float on that industry. Not only did it put a bomb under it (to the extent that what exists now would be unrecognisable to those who witnessed the invention), but it took the industry completely by surprise.

The float process is the Holy Grail of the flat glass industry. Its discovery represents one of the great inventions of the industrial twentieth century. The glass produced by this process is perfect – it is distortion free, brightly fire-finished, and cheap. Almost all the clear flat glass in the world is now made by this process. It is as if the sheer guts and loyalty of everyone in the company, over many years, to this stuff called glass was to qualify them to receive the victor's crown. It is not possible to imagine a superior process for making a flat glass ribbon. Float catapulted the company, and the name Pilkington, into world prominence.

The Pilkingtons were part of that great Victorian industrial movement of family enterprises, Cadbury, Lever, Rowntree, which grew up during the nineteenth century. The businesses they pioneered developed into colossi. They set high standards of business behaviour towards their workers, customers and communities. They took long-term views. They were Nonconformists – Quakers, Congregationalists. They were barred by this commitment from top professions such as the law.

Much of the Pilkington story has already been written competently by others, from various points of view. So why bother to do it again?

Because I was there! I was a family member and a director. I witnessed the inside story. I was embedded in that story. As the last family director still (2010) alive, who lived and worked in St Helens, I saw, at first hand, the transition from a family business to an international corporation, and the heroic efforts required to develop and implement float. I experienced at first hand the fascinating interplay between the family and this mysterious stuff called glass.

I was never a leader, or a tycoon. My role seemed to be that of listener and carer. There is much similarity here to the role of my father, Guy, a member of the third generation. We both played our part, but appear minimally in all the histories.

The invention and development of float are described in Chapter 11, 'Float: The Holy Grail'. That chapter is in one sense the most 'authentic' in the whole book, as it is based on my direct experience. Alastair Pilkington, the inventor of the float process, joined the company in 1947. Our careers covered the same time span, 1947 to 1980, and some of the time we worked closely together. We were both Engineers. I make no claim to share in the glory that was float. My work was in the field of human relations, but as an engineer I understood the technology of glassmaking and have tried to explain it in this book.

My source is mainly my own (fallible) memory, but backed up by some authoritative documents and books which I have listed in the References. This work is authentic in the sense that it is a memoir of my life immersed in the Pilkington Thing. It makes no claim to be scholarly although all facts have been checked by knowledgeable people. It is written for my grandchildren. It is written for fun. But it is also written as an acknowledgement of the immense effort and loyalty of all those who worked for the company.

Only two of the colleagues I worked with are mentioned by name in this text – the chief players Sir Harry Pilkington (later Lord Pilkington) and Sir Alastair Pilkington. Other names will appear where this is essential for the text. The other, unnamed supportive and wonderful people whom I worked with and valued were hundreds (literally hundreds) of loyal, hard-working folk, at *all* levels, those indispensable ones who took the ideas of the chief players and made them work. And then, of course, there are those who, throughout the pages of history, built the enterprise over 170 years.

It seems surprising that the two industrial giants Sir Harry and Sir Alastair Pilkington lack full-length biographies devoted to their individual lives. Both have entries in the *National Dictionary of Biography* containing only limited accounts of the influences which shaped their destinies. Perhaps the answer, as we will see, is that they cannot be separated. Harry needed Alastair, and Alastair needed Harry. Harry was made chairman of the company in 1949 just before the moment (1952) when Alastair invented float. Harry needed Alastair to provide him with the ultimate commercial weapon. Alastair needed Harry to provide him with the money. I don't think they liked each other, but they worked wonderfully well together.

We will hear of triumphs and setbacks. There will be three takeover bids for the company. There will be important serendipity. There will be an assassination attempt on a chairman. We will hear how the float process was patented fifty years before it worked. There will be major top-level conflicts within the family (why are rows always news?), one of which is known in family folklore as the 'Big Row'. There will be references throughout to various ways of making flat glass. There will be reference to the thread which ran through the whole saga, which held it together and which, I believe, was the source of any greatness. I have called this the Soul of Pilkington, and it is epitomised by the adoption of James Pilkington, Prince Bishop of Durham (*c.*1520–75), as a family emblem.

Every business, like every person, has elements and episodes which are forgettable and usually swept under the proverbial carpet. The story of the Glass Act, to be true to its nature, has to be transparent. There will be some sensitive bits. There will be some 'naughty' bits. If anybody is in any way hurt by any of the comments, please forgive.

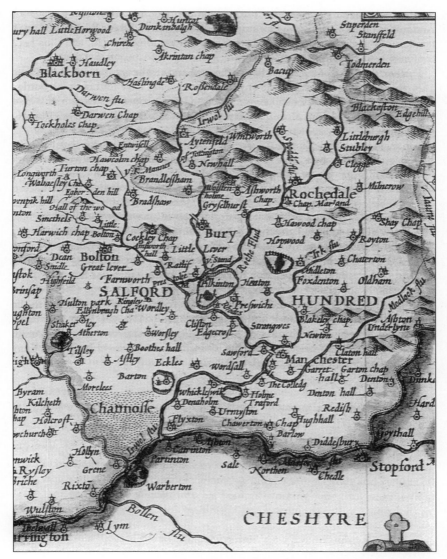

Figure 1   Detail of 1610 map of Lancashire showing Pilkington Park

Before we get going on the saga of the Glass Act, there are two basic questions which need answering. What is this thing called glass? And who are these folk called Pilkington?

This mysterious stuff called glass *is* truly mysterious. It is at one and the same time both solid and liquid. It is as strong as high-tensile steel. It is as light as aluminium. In the form of revolving wet wine glasses it becomes a musical instrument (a glass harmonica). Mozart wrote for it! This most ancient of materials is today at the technological forefront in the form of the solar cells of spacecraft and the fibre optics of communication. It has ever-lasting qualities, but in certain forms can also dissolve in water. (Grandmother used it to store her eggs.) Its transparency is matched by that of other materials such as perspex, but at the cost of softness, expensiveness and rapid chemical degradation.

These folk with the funny name came from a place called Pilkington just north-west of Manchester (Figure 1). The Pilkingtons took their name from the place. The name derives from the proper name Pilk, *ing* (people), and *ton* (settlement): 'Pilk's people's place'. The branch who became glassmakers moved to St Helens, Lancashire in the late 1780s and took the plunge into glassmaking in 1826.

And finally, there is something more to this story than first meets the eye. The Pilkington family, with their strong pious tendencies, found in glass a matching character. Glass in most of its manifestations is a 'servant' material, particularly in the form the Pilkingtons specialised in – flat glass. Boring in many ways, not much to write home about, best when unnoticed. But the window ranks an important second to the most basic human needs, for food, clothing and shelter. That part of your shelter has a transparent bit to let in light (while keeping out the cold) is rather important.

A drinking glass has a similar servant quality. Glass vessels, retorts, test tubes, distillation columns, were essential to science. Galileo transformed the whole of religious thought by using glass in a series of connected lenses extended into a telescope to undermine the paradigm of the Earth as the centre of the universe by observing three celestial objects circling round another celestial object – Jupiter and its planets.

For us, to be making such a marvellous and essential material put the business in which the Pilkingtons engaged into a special category. We loved glass. We loved the great furnaces that melted the raw materials. We loved the machines that turned that molten mass into a product. No better is this love demonstrated than in the life of Cecil Pilkington, a leader of the third generation. He slept in the works. He wouldn't go home! (See Chapter 5.)

Part One

Through a Glass Distortedly:
From the Beginnings to Float

Chapter One

The First Generation: The Founders (1826–1860)

The story starts with a Dr William Pilkington, from whose loins two of the main players in the story were to emerge. Dr William was not involved with glass. He was a medical man. It was his children who took the first step. He was my great-great-grandfather.

The subject of this chapter is basically his children, Richard and William – whom I have called the first generation – but it is helpful to say something about their father. Dr William (1765–1831) had many children, fifteen in total (seven sons, seven daughters and one child out of wedlock), nearly half of whom were to die as children. Going back still further, there was Dr William's grandfather, called Richard (1694–1786), a small farmer in Horwich who had come into an inheritance, a mansion, land, farms – in a word, money. This inheritance allowed his grandson, William, to go to London to train as a doctor and then return to the North West in the late 1780s to set up a medical practice in St Helens, Lancashire.

William was a doctor, a surgeon and an apothecary, who distilled alcohol for medical reasons, as a solvent from which to produce medicines and as an anaesthetic. As a surgeon he needed to have the only anaesthetic available at that time – alcohol, combined with other available drugs such as laudanum. His father's diary refers to him removing the 'brest' of the wife of 'Isac', his father's labourer.

The story of that unfortunate lady gives a feel for what life was like in those days. We romanticise them now, but they were short, tough and brutish. The St Helens air was a permanent lethal smog. The sewage system was primitive to say the least. Everything either lay about in cesspits or emptied into the Sankey Valley Stream (the 'Stinking Brook' as my father called it). Outbreaks of cholera and typhoid occurred from time to time.

In some ways life in those days was not noteworthy. St Helens was not untypical in terms of infant mortality. No doubt future generations will opine that the early twenty-first century was a rough, tough time in which to live.

What may seem surprising to us in the twenty-first century is that a part of Dr William's medical practice was the production of alcohol, not unusual in the eighteenth century. Over the years this branch of his medical activities flourished and became a successful business in its own right, so much so that his sons, Richard and William (Plate 1), started their working lives managing, in effect, a distillery and an off-licence.

Of Dr William's other children, little is known to me. Some of his other sons had careers in fields other than alcohol or glass. One of his daughters, Eleanor, married a Peter Greenall who was to make a key financial input into the later glass industry. Dr William's father complained bitterly in a letter of his displeasure at his illegitimate grandchild. Apart from that, little is known, except about the men, Richard and William.

So now to the story of the first generation. It was William, the younger son of Dr William, who initiated the connection between the Pilkingtons and this strange material called glass. He spent his time as a young man with his elder brother managing their father's alcohol business. As all throughout history have found, alcohol is profitable. So much so that Dr William himself gave up doctoring to concentrate with his sons on manufacturing and selling a recreational substance which probably caused more harm in the nineteenth century than any other. It was a strange switch for his family from doing good with medicine to doing harm with alcohol. Did it trouble their consciences? The answer must be 'yes' because the next generation became serious temperance movement followers.

Left: Richard Pilkington, co-founder, 1795–1869
Right: William Pilkington, co-founder, 1800–1872

Plate 1 The founders

Richard, the elder brother, was certainly pious. He spent every Sunday teaching in the Sunday school and in church attendance. He was a Nonconformist (Congregational). He had made a fortunate marriage to a wealthy and intelligent lady called Ann Evans. I have nicknamed him 'Stay-at-home'. Ann will appear again and she will keep the label 'Ann Evans'.

Richard was a gentle, reliable character, not in any way a businessman. He and Ann produced six sons. The two eldest, William ('Windle Will') and Richard ('Rainford Richard'), went into glass, the other four into the other family business, coal. We will read of all of them again in the chapter on the second generation.

Richard's household was the perfect nursery for talent. According to the youngest son, Lawrence, theirs was a singularly happy and harmonious home, any little difficulty or boyish prank on their part being smoothed over by their mother, Ann. And the needs of glass and coal were there to spur them all.

Richard continued with alcohol, the profits feeding into the foray of his younger brother, William, into glass. Richard was later to join the glass business. He was my great-grandfather.

William, the younger son, was outstandingly energetic and resourceful. He had contributed hugely to alcohol and came up with the solution to the brothers' rather nice problem of what to do with the surplus cash from the alcohol business. I have nicknamed him 'Go-getter'. He was a solid rock (finance, technical, selling) on which the great enterprise started life. His elder brother was an essential helper in supporting, but William was the spearhead. (See his obituary, Appendix 7.)

Today, cash is invested in a vast range of possibilities, but in 1826 the range was extremely limited – coal, canals, shipping, banks and government stocks. It was too early for railways (the Stockton and Darlington Railway carried its first passengers only a year before).

There was, however, a new kid on the block – glass, or, more precisely, flat glass. Flat glass had in fact been made, by what is known as the crown process, for around two thousand years, but demand was now increasing exponentially. The industrial revolution was gathering momentum, with the big demand for new housing, as people moved from the countryside to the new towns in search of work. Since St Helens was one of those new towns, it was natural that a glassworks should be established there to service the building boom. It was, accordingly, in 1826 that the first glassworks were built there, in which William was prevailed upon to take a share (Plate 2). St Helens was to boast three glassworks up until 1870. There were other glassworks on Tyneside, Birmingham and Scotland, in total about twenty.

There was another good reason why St Helens had glassworks. St Helens sat on extensive coal deposits. One ton of glass required ten tons of coal to melt its ingredients.

The glass business was given a big fillip by the removal in 1851 of an early attempt at an income tax system – the Window Tax – where your ability to pay was measured by the number of windows you had in your house. Glass was double taxed, with a second tax (excise duty) paid by the glassmaker on the quantity of glass manufactured in the glassworks. It is not clear why glassmaking was so targeted by two forms of tax.

Plate 2   Exterior of the first glasshouse

One important Pilkington contact was Peter Greenall, who had married Richard and William's sister, Eleanor. He was already in alcohol, owning a brewery in St Helens (later to become the modern Greenall Whitley). Peter had invested his spare cash in glass – the St Helens Crown Glass Company – so 'Go-getter' William followed his brother-in-law's lead and joined him in that investment. His elder brother, Richard, joined nine years later.

The St Helens Crown Glass Company had not yet actually sold any glass, and soon it became evident to William Pilkington and Peter Greenall that the existing management was incompetent. The new glassworks, instead of being an investment, was looking more like a 'sink'. William was forced to get involved. No longer an investment, that glassworks became his livelihood and his life.

Such was his involvement that William built an office-cum-bedroom in the works. Dissatisfied with the glassworkers' performance, he slept in the factory (see Cecil Pilkington doing the same two generations later, but for a different reason). You can imagine the effect on the men when the boss turned up at any time, day or night!

As well as imposing this primitive and effective management style, William took on an engineer, James Kenmore, who proved to be the man of the moment and when promoted to the top management job turned the company round (see William's obituary, Appendix 6). William, now free of works management, could go out into the world and get orders.

Tribute has to be paid to Peter Greenall, not only for introducing the Pilkingtons to glass, but also because his financial strength and credibility were invaluable in those early, insecure, embryo days. The Greenalls were already prominent local landowners. Peter was in charge of their affairs in St Helens (including the brewery) and was using his influential position to exercise a benevolent despotism over the town's development. After

Richard joined his younger brother, the Pilkingtons took an increasingly central role until all the other partners, including Peter Greenall, sold out. In 1847 the Pilkingtons had asked Peter for a loan, which soured relationships (Williams-Ellis 1997, p. 68). Peter had decided to stand for Parliament, and to dispose of his share in the glassworks in order to finance this.

The two Pilkington brothers were a successful team. 'Go-getter' William went out into the world, searching for business and new methods of manufacture. 'Stay-at-home' Richard had the role that suited him – making sure the wages were paid, the raw materials ordered, the quality of the glass controlled and the accounts properly kept.

Theo Barker says that Richard does not seem to have taken too kindly to the hurly-burly of business, but that he was an ideal business associate for William, as someone in whom he could have complete trust looking after the home front. William gently chides his elder brother in a letter of 1834, 'You under-rate yourself and your abilities sadly too much.'

With such divergent characters, one can imagine discussions between the brothers about the nature of business. Was it solely about making money, or was there some deeper meaning. There is direct evidence of a considerable difference of view between the brothers on such questions.

William unfurled his colours once the enterprise showed signs of mature success. He made a takeover bid for the business by appointing his eldest son as a partner. His aim was to bring his sons in as partners with full voting rights, and keep his brother's children 'in their place' as managers and barred from any position of power.

As the more forceful of the two brothers, William very nearly succeeded in his purpose. It was Richard's wife, Ann (Evans), who is reported to have said to her husband 'Don't let them do it!'. She pressed her husband into writing a letter to his brother to that effect. The letter, dated 1865, exists and is shown in Figure 2. Within days of that letter, Richard's two children were appointed partners, to balance the two children of William, and an agreement was made of only two partners from each family.

This crucial incident is interesting on two counts. The first is that it shows clearly how women exercised their influence in those days. Cut off from direct involvement in the business, they worked behind the scenes. This old-fashioned attitude to women continued through to the fifth generation. As an active member of the fourth generation, I recall that the question of a family woman becoming a member of the board was never ever considered. There were only a handful of (non-family) women in senior management even in my time. Family women expressed no obvious desire.

The second count on which this incident is interesting is that is shows the difference between the two brothers, a difference which was to influence future generations. The descendants of Richard tended to take long-term views and to see the business as a calling. William's descendants had more short-term ideas, seeing the business as a goose which laid golden eggs and which was there to provide jobs for male family members and adornments for their ladies. This may be an unfair conclusion. It is certainly true that William's descendants were the more prolific and genuinely required more cash to support them. Further evidence of this split can be observed in the second generation, when there was serious argument about whether the company should embark on the manufacture of plate glass. Again, Ann Evans (Plate 3) is involved.

As a result of this dichotomy, arguably, Richard's branch increased in power. The towering figures of the Pilkington history – 'Windle Will' Pilkington and Sir Harry Pilkington – came from it. The descendants of 'Go-getter' William over time made less and less impact on the business. Although one finds oneself taking sides, dichotomies have their positive side in sharpening the arguments and clarifying thinking.

Having resolved the partnership issue, the Pilkingtons were able to concentrate on the manufacture and the sale of glass. Letters from 'Go-getter' William came in regularly to St Helens, goading 'Stay-at-home' Richard to do a better job with more care and attention to the quality of the glass and promptness of delivery.

Although there was a rapidly growing demand for their product, there were other manufacturers in the field. There were around seventeen other glassmakers in the country, three of which were located in St Helens. The North East (Hartley) was also strong in the industry, as was the Midlands, where Chance Brothers held sway.

For the fledgling business, nothing was easy. As well as home-grown competitors, the international trade was developing, particularly from Belgium. This latter country had a major glass industry, trading on three legs – great beds of high-quality sand, coal without limit and easy access to the sea (as well as the European waterways).

Pilkington was similarly situated on sand and coal, but not as well endowed as competitors in Belgium. Access to the sea was through the port of Liverpool. Salt came from the great deposits in Cheshire up the newly built Sankey Canal to meet with coal (and glass) in St Helens.

The 'foreigners', as the Pilkingtons called the Belgians, were always 'a thorn in the flesh'. They were accused of having nasty habits. One, they worked on the Sabbath, and two, they did not stick to commercial agreements.

Very soon after the start, the Pilkingtons were faced with a revolutionary change in the manufacture of their flat glass.

18th March 1865

Windle Hall
St. Helens
Lancashire

My dear Will,

Thinking over our interview on Saturday, I feel as strongly if not more so, that my son William should be placed upon the same footing in the Concern as your son, who has now been a partner for 11 or 12 years; I made not the least objection to his joining us understanding that my two sons would have the same privilege as your two at the proper time, and it is no fault of mine that your son Thomas is not a partner. I shall not be satisfied until my son William is a partner. I do not wish to use hard words, there were plenty of them the other day, at the same time I cannot be silent. I do not see that any resolution you may make without my consent, where the interest of myself and family are concerned, can be binding on me; I trust you will reconsider what passed on Saturday. Do not let any alienation take place between us in our old age. I cannot relinquish so just a claim as this and you cannot in justice or honour object to it.

As to your remarks on money affairs I find by the books that in 1827 when we entered into the Glass Works, we were owing little or nothing to any one, as Preston's and other Accounts were as nearly balanced as possible and there were no mortgages on any of the property. With the landed and other property including the Concern, there was above £30,000 put into the Glassworks, the particulars I gave at the close. We were working on this property 4 years before my father's death, and then Thos Pilkington's and P. Greenall's legacies £4000 were paid out with the former's profit of £1000 when he left the Concern. My Sisters money is still in our hands, which has much increased after supporting them.

Figure 2   'Don't let them do it!': letter from Richard
Pilkington to William Pilkington

Most well managed concerns with such capital will often exceed the amount we have made; again excepting just after the duty came off, our profits these last three years have been greater than ever they were before. The average of the three has been double any of the preceding ones.

For my own part, I have always given my best attention to the business, and never crippled the Concern by drawing money out. Indeed, it has been otherwise, for I have had £3000 of my wife's money for more than seventeen years in the Concern. Added to this the Messrs. Evans offered me a partnership with them, but as it was to myself alone and not for you as well, I declined it. They have also at different times offered to take William as partner, this also I have declined as I naturally wished to keep him at the Works, where my prosperity is. If he does not take his place at the Works as partner, I shall have done him injustice, you know the difference between a Master and Servant as well as I do.

I wish to explain one thing that passed on Saturday as to partnerships, what I intended to convey was this, a partner in two establishments if one be unsuccessful, it may interfere with his property in the other, unless there be suitable provision to prevent it. Where many members of a family are concerned this possibility should be provided for.

I shall furnish your sons William and Thomas with a copy of this letter, as I do not think they have a clear understanding of the money left by their Grandfather, and what money has come into the Concern in other ways.

I remain
your affectionate brother
(Signed) Richard Pilkington

Figure 2   'Don't let them do it!' (cont.)

Plate 3   Ann Evans

Up until this point, molten glass had been gathered on the end of a blowpipe, blown into a bubble and then spun out into a 'crown' (Figure 3), which was then cut into panes (Figure 4). Now, however, instead of gathering molten glass on the end of a blowpipe and blowing a bubble and spinning it into a 6' disc, the idea emerged of hanging the bubble over a pit and allowing gravity to elongate it into a cylinder. The 'blown cylinder' process produced much larger pieces of glass (Figure 5). Big arguments raged for years over which was the better process. In the end, however, the blown cylinder prevailed.

The glass industry, like most other industries at that time, was man's work. There was virtually no mechanisation. It was reported by an observer at that time that, in addition to being able to manipulate a heavy lump of molten glass on the end of a blowpipe and blowing it into a cylinder, the top blowers could swing their cylinder over their heads with a 360-degree arc. Mighty men of valour! Without question, there was no room for women on the factory floor.

As related earlier, however, there was one woman who had a major continuing influence on the business, Ann Evans. She continued to be consulted, as she grew older, by the first generation as they continued to face the problems of running a business, and the second generation also kept in touch with her.

Although there certainly were problems for the business, there was one area of industry where the bosses did have a somewhat easy time. The trade union movement had not yet become established. The owners could treat labour as they liked. If they wanted to hire an expert glassblower, they could pay him a relatively high wage, or could reward a 'good servant' uniquely and individually with a pension, and, of course, they could more easily fire people. Labour was, as yet, unorganised, although the first stirrings of socialism were occurring in the Chartist movement and affecting industry in Manchester, only twenty miles away. St Helens remained a calm backwater.

There were other areas where the owners had a lot of freedom. Government controls were few. There was a minimal Income Tax, introduced to pay for the Napoleonic Wars. There was the Window Tax. There were Acts of Parliament protecting child labour, requiring machines to be guarded, setting up three more Bank Holidays and providing compensation for industrial injuries. There was an important Act preventing employers paying workers with tokens to be spent only in company shops. But Health and Safety were left to the individual employer. In the dangerous handling of glass (all manual, no mechanisation) there were awful accidents; the company doctor was always a surgeon, skilled at rejoining tendons. Protective clothing developed and improved over the years but, short of a suit of armour, nothing gave total protection.

There were absolutely no pollution controls. The air of St Helens must have been particularly foul with industry, railways and domestic dwellings all burning coal inefficiently. Also, the chemical industry was responsible for belching particularly obnoxious fumes. When I was a boy, before the Second World War, from a hill outside St Helens, at Fenney Bank Farm, I could count 157 chimneys. On the same spot today I could count ten. Until the 1953 Clean Air Act we had to go home early on some autumn afternoons because you literally couldn't see the kerb to drive your car.

When the Sankey Canal was built in 1775 to connect St Helens coal to Cheshire salt, the usual practice of locking a river was not followed. The local river, the Sankey Brook, was judged too unreliable as to its flow and too foul as to its quality to use as a feeder for a locked river (a 'navigation'), so it was decided to cut a new artificial waterway fed with a separate clean water supply and eight locks to raise the water level.

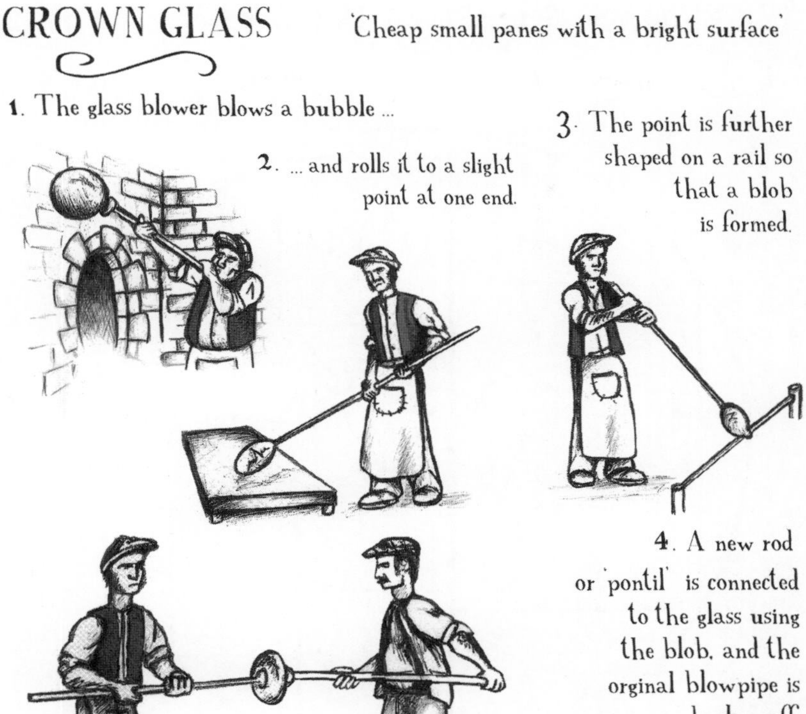

CROWN GLASS 'Cheap small panes with a bright surface'

1. The glass blower blows a bubble ...

2. ... and rolls it to a slight point at one end.

3. The point is further shaped on a rail so that a blob is formed.

4. A new rod or 'pontil' is connected to the glass using the blob, and the orginal blowpipe is broken off.

5. The bubble of glass is reheated and spun out into a 'crown' on the new rod.

6. The crown is then cut into panes (Figure 4).

Figure 3   Crown glass

CUTTING OF A CROWN INTO PANES

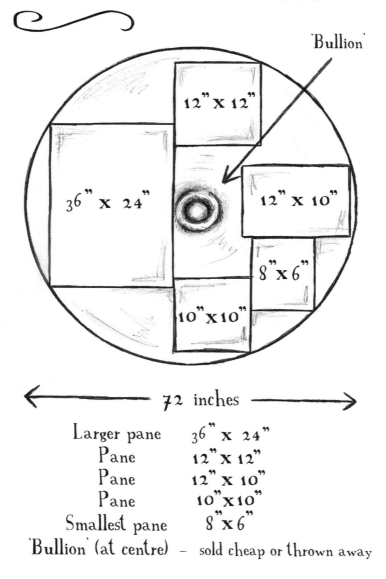

Figure 4   Cutting of a crown into panes

Larger pane	36" x 24"
Pane	12" x 12"
Pane	12" x 10"
Pane	10" x 10"
Smallest pane	8" x 6"
'Bullion' (at centre)	– sold cheap or thrown away

CYLINDER BLOWN 'Cheap, large panes, with marred surfaces'

1. The glass blower dips a blowpipe through the 'Glory Hole' to gather a large blob of molten glass.

2. The glass blob is blown into a bubble, which is flattened out slightly.

3. The glass blower continues to work and reheat the glass, swinging it in a long trench to form an elongated cylinder.

4. The completed cylinder is cut and flattened out into a sheet, marring the surface.

Weight of cylinder: 56 lb
Area of flattened cylinder: 28 sq. ft

Figure 5   Cylinder blown

The Sankey Canal was the first true canal, the pioneer of the great British canal system which was so crucial in forging the industrial revolution. It is one of St Helens' claims to fame, arguably a more important claim than being the cradle of the Glass Act. It was operating four years before Brindley's much-publicised canal from Worsley to Manchester, and no doubt he was able to observe it.

Other St Helens' claims to fame were Beecham's Pills ('worth a guinea a box') and Sir Thomas Beecham, third generation of that family. His debut as a conductor was with the Hallé Orchestra in St Helens town hall at the age of nineteen (their celebrated conductor, Hans Richter, being indisposed). Not yet knighted, he lived with his parents in the St Helens area, but was obviously demonstrating talent. St Helens also fathered Richard Seddon, who emigrated aged eighteen and became prime minister of New Zealand at the turn of the nineteenth century. He returned twice to a tumultuous welcome, in 1897 for Victoria's Diamond Jubilee and in 1902 for the coronation of Edward VII.

Our Glass Act is still in its early stages and the second generation is poised for action. Thanks to Ann Evans the transition was seamless. Thanks to her intervention, the succession fell to four people, the two sons of the two founders, William Windle, Rainford Richard, William Roby and Thomas. We will hear of the 'Four' in the next chapter.

The first generation could now retire, knowing that they had set up a potentially thriving business. Their early vision and stickability had been well rewarded. In 1860, Pilkington was still a small-town business, tiny compared with what it was to become 100 years later. The seed had been sown, however, and a sturdy tree now stood firm amid the feverish activity called the industrial revolution, a tree nourished by a culture of entrepreneurial courage and tenacity of purpose which was to become the hallmark of the company.

'Stay-at-home' Richard continued to live in St Helens at Windle Hall until his death. 'Go-getter' William moved to North Wales. The scene was now set for the generation that was to consolidate and lay the foundations of the future colossus and, in particular, for the ultimate flowering of the Glass Act, the invention of the float process.

Chapter Two

Sandcastles (Fantasy Number 1)

A fantasy on a holiday beach near Dartmouth, Devon. A fantasy based on fact, but nevertheless, a fantasy.

(*Fantasy in italics.* Reality in roman.)

[On the beach.]

'Grandpa.'

'Yes, dear.'

'Wasn't that the best ever sandcastle we made yesterday?'

'Yes dear, the best ever.'

'What else can you do with sand, Grandpa?'

'Lots of things. Would you like to hear about what some brave people did with sand, thousands of years ago?'

'Yes please. Were you there?'

'No, dear, it happened long before I was born.'

'Go on, Grandpa.'

'My story starts at a seaport, like Dartmouth, but a long way south on the northern shores of Africa where it's very hot. Summer all year round. My story is about a handsome young man called Solomon.

Little did he know that he was about to be part of one of the greatest discoveries in history.

The only son of a wealthy trader, Solomon came from a long line of sea-going folk based in Alexandria, Egypt. He was a Phoenician and his forebears had sailed around much of the known world. His father had trained him in navigating skills and now, satisfied with his progress, had helped him to build his own boat.

As well as constructing the boat, Solomon had spent much time puzzling about what his purpose in life should be. One purpose he knew very well – he wanted to find a girl to accompany him on his voyages of discovery. There was Farida. Was she the one?

He had to decide soon. And then, there was the family business of salt trading. Was that the life for him? Again, he knew he had to make an early decision.

It was an overcast day when Solomon decided to set out on the journey from Alexandria to Venice. His ship was loaded with salt. His new ship, with up-to-date sails and rigging, was fast and seaworthy and this was the foundation of his hopes. It was winter and he knew the eastern Mediterranean was subject to short, violent storms, but his ship was seaworthy. He also knew that the wind tended to blow steadily from the east in winter.

The destination of his voyage was Venice. Venice was a new, fast-growing city and the wealthy were crying out for what he had to bring. Salt. Common salt was highly sought-after in the ancient world, not only for flavouring but also for food preservation. No fridges in those days. In Alexandria there were regions where seawater was left in the heat of the sun to evaporate leaving the salt behind. This was cut up into cakes. It was these cakes that were being loaded into Sol's ship.

'How's it going?', Solomon shouted to Jason, his first mate, who was supervising the loading of the cargo.

'Well, sir. We should be ready to sail tomorrow at dawn.'

'Good. Sooner the better to catch these winds.'

Sol's ship had a decent cabin built in, so he was taking his new bride with him. Sol was troubled about his first mate. Jason was an old seafarer. He was muttering that it was bad luck to have a woman on board ship. He was also anxious because this new ship had not been blessed by the priest.

But Sol was young and thrusting. He had no time for old-fashioned superstitions. He wanted to be away. There was money to be made. He reasoned with his first mate, 'Cheer up, Jason. No need to be so gloomy. We've got a brand new seaworthy vessel. You've had it out to sea and satisfied yourself. Farida will be a great asset. She's saved us money already from having to pay for a cook. Wait till you've tasted her food.'

The wind held, the cargo was complete and the ship sailed at dawn the next day.

Unfortunately, Jason's predictions were only too correct, and within two days the wind had turned. In spite of its modern rigging, the ship was unable to beat against the storm. They were forced to beach it off the Palestinian coast. Listing badly, but undamaged, the ship lay helpless as the tide receded.

Sol surveyed the desolate scene. Worse still, his leg had become trapped by shifting cargo. He was in low spirits but buoyed up by his conviction about the salt trade and his other conviction about Farida. Farida had leapt into the gap and taken firm charge of the situation. Jason was too open-mouthed to challenge her. Within a few hours, Farida had got a stockpot boiling on a cheerful fire on the shore. She had given orders to bring a number of salt blocks from the ship to fashion a hearth for the stockpot. No rocks on this sandy shore.

Stiff, cold and tired, they woke next day to an offshore wind. Not only in the right direction, but warm and gentle. There was hope of *refloating on the next tide. Sol felt sure his luck had turned.*

'Look at this!', Farida called to him. Sol hobbled over to the fireplace.

'What on earth is it?'

The hearth, now cold, looked as though it were sitting in molten sugar. Sol recognised the stuff as similar to some volcanic rock he had seen in a jar maker's workshop. The jar maker had heated and softened the rock and turned it into rods which he had then wrapped round sand cores to make storage vessels. But Sol saw something else. The stuff on the beach was different from the volcanic rock. Although full of bubbles and unmelted material, it was clear. Unlike volcanic rock, this stuff was transparent.

'Leave it, sir.' The first mate was impatient to catch the tide. 'We don't want to put weight back on board.'

But something told Sol that this stuff was important. He struggled to break a piece off the molten mass. The port where the salt was unloaded was Venice. It was to Venice that that first piece of man-made glass was taken. It was Venice, where people already skilled in the exploitation of volcanic rock took Sol's discovery through the next crucial step.

The first step had been taken. A mixture of salt and sand is heated. The salt melts first and the sand dissolves in it like sugar in water. Limestone is added to the mix to give the glass its permanency. Experiments with the man-made glass reached the point where white-hot ceramic pots of clear, fault-free molten glass were available to turn into high-quality rods to wrap round sand cores. And then, someone dipped a *hollow* metal tube or pipe into a ceramic pot of molten glass, gathered a glob on the end and *blew*! Date around 3000 BC.

Recognised by all historians as the most crucial step in the whole history of glassmaking is the invention of the blowpipe. Now, via blowing, a drinking or storage vessel could be created quickly and cheaply. But, obviously, not a flat piece of glass.

Then, at a much later date, maybe 2000 BC, a second crucial invention: the bubble was spun to form a flat circular disc out of which windows could be cut (Figures 3, 4).

'Phew! Thanks, Grandpa.'

'It is a strange story, isn't it? Nobody knows for sure what actually happened or when. It must have been something like that.'

'Grandpa?'

'Yes, dear.'

'You make glass, don't you?'

'Yes dear.'

'Will you show me?'

'Not yet, dear. Glassmakers don't allow women in their factory, but family is different, so when you're sixteen, I'll take you then.'

Chapter Three

The Second Generation:
The Consolidators (1860–1894)

It could be argued that the second generation of the Pilkingtons was the most crucial group in the whole of the story. It is one thing to start a business; it is quite another to establish it solidly and successfully into the second generation of the family. There is a big question – will there be sons (it had to be sons!) capable of picking up the baton? Will those sons have the vision and the energy and the courage of their forebears? Will they be able to carry the baton and hand it on to the third generation?

As we have seen in the previous chapter, the forebears of the second generation brought an intense dedication to their calling, but they also had Lady Luck shining on them in the shape of external finances suckling the infant business – Ann Evans' £3,000 (equivalent to £750,000 in today's money), and continuing profits from alcohol. Another important thing about the second generation's birth was that the question of succession had been well decided before the first generation withdrew from active involvement, and with the powerful Ann Evans still there to be consulted.

Each of the founders, 'Stay-at-home' Richard and 'Go-getter' William, left two sons to follow in their footsteps (Figure 6; Plate 4). The names they were given can lead to confusion, so I will continue the habit of giving nicknames. 'Stay-at-home' Richard had two sons:

William, who we will call 'Windle Will' (WW). This is the actual nickname by which he was known by his contemporaries.

Richard, who we will call 'Rainford Richard' (RR).

'Go-getter' William had two sons:

William, who we will call 'Roby Bill', as he was actually known by his contemporaries.

Thomas, who we will call 'Thomas'.

The non-Pilkington partners were soon all bought out, the last of them being the influential Peter Greenall, whose access to funds had been so helpful in the early days. The name over the door became 'Pilkington Brothers' in 1845. 'Pilkington Brothers' became 'Pilkington Brothers Ltd' in 1894.

The concept of limited liability ('Ltd') was an important foundation stone for the thriving business. Invented by King James I in the seventeenth century, it meant that the 'Four' were no longer 'partners' but 'shareholders'. In the case of business failure the shareholders lost only the money they had invested rather than, as partners, the whole of their wealth. So one can easily see the potential benefit to any business not yet fully established. Limited liability also opened up a further potential benefit, that of increasing the value of an existing business to more shareholders.

This chapter is the story of the 'Four', the second generation of the Pilkington family which put the company firmly on the map. At the start of the tenure there were seventeen flat glass companies in England, and at the end only two, the other being Chance Brothers.

Little is known to me about Thomas, except that his inclination was to 'eat the seed corn' rather than plough the profits back into the business. Thomas retired in 1898 after four years as chairman.

He owned a famous racehorse (Prince Palatine), winner of most of the top races and valued at nearly £40,000. After Thomas sold him on to another owner, that story came to a sad end when the horse was due to take part in the Kentucky Derby but died in a fire at the stables before the event.

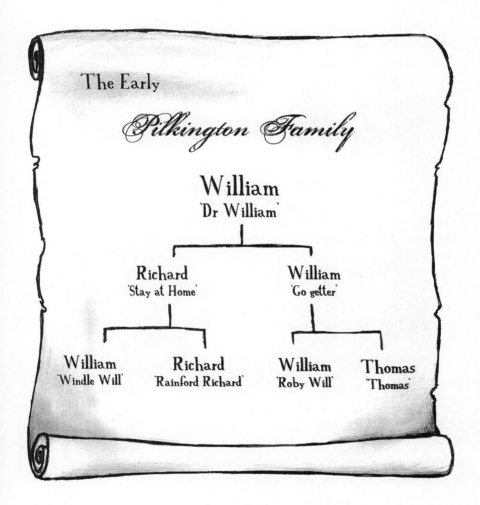

Figure 6   The early Pilkington family

Roby Bill became involved more in politics than in business. He was a Deputy Lieutenant of Lancashire in 1887 and turned down a baronetcy in 1892. He was a good businessman, and no doubt was an important foil for Windle Will in debates between the partners, but his heart was elsewhere.

William Windle Pilkington

Richard Pilkington

William (Roby) Pilkington

Thomas Pilkington

Plate 4   The second generation: the 'Four'

Blood has various thicknesses and the brothers' blood was thicker than the cousins'! Roby Bill and Thomas tended to stick together, as did Rainford Richard and Windle Will. The antagonism between the camps came to a head in 1875, only ten years after the previous battle. The cousins – Roby Bill and Thomas –

were for opening the company up to outside shareholders in order to distribute more of the profits. They were against entering into the risky and costly manufacture of plate glass.

Windle Will and Rainford Richard won the argument. The entry into plate was one of the most significant events of the Glass Act. The letter from Rainford Richard to his mother, Ann Evans, shown in Figure 7 illustrates some of the tension. The company could now completely satisfy the market with the full range of transparent flat glass. This was a vital step towards float.

My dear Mama,

It would be wrong not to write to you to tell you, of what passed here.

On the day I saw you I went to Liverpool and saw Hawkins (Partner in the Legal firm, Forshaw and Hawkins). Pears, their [William and Thomas's] lawyer, had come down to Liverpool on purpose to try and settle.

I ought perhaps, as you are so very much interested and this is the completion of what has been a two month struggle, to tell you how the end has come. On Saturday we told Cousin Will that he could not go to Vienna unless he signed. He said, 'If you pay my courier I will stay.' we said. 'No. Your courier is your own affair and we will not.'

On Saturday we had a consultation in Hawkins' office which resulted in him writing to Pears to say such was the utmost we could do and the matter must be settled. On Monday I saw both Cousins and they were told that if I sent to London with Hawkins to see Pears, it must be settled one way or the other. In the afternoon of Monday Tom received a telegram from Pears saying he would be down and must meet him in L'pool and bring their Cousin (that was me). We went in. Hawkins saw Pears. They conceded everything but the Plate Glass Clause. Will and I saw Hawkins on Tuesday and agreed with him that all must go up to London and settle. We met at the Westminster Palace at 4. We began at 4.30, Pears, Hawkins and we four. We sat for 3 hours. Pears was very stiff about the Plate Glass Clause, so was Tom most obstinate. We were also stiff. They went out of the room at nearly 8 o'clock, came back, said they would not consent. Hawkins buttoned his coat and said, 'Then there's the other alternative', meaning dissolution. I then broke in and reproached them with not meeting us. They then agreed to the clause with no alteration, which Hawkins had suggested before they left the room.

Hawkins and Sinclair drew up the clause in an agreement. We went to the Palace Hotel this morning. Pears came in first. Hawkins and he read it through. Then the

---

Figure 7   '… it must be settled …': letter from
Richard Pilkington to Ann Evans

Cousins came in and at last Pears said, 'I think it's alright. I must explain to my clients.' We went out and waited a long time. We began to fear they were again trying to strike the clause or remodel it, taking the strength out of it, but we now think Cousin Will and Pears were convincing Tom. At last we were called back. Then Hawkins and Pears talked and we agreed to some verbal alteration, which was fair and practically left the clause as we previously had it. We then signed. We got everything we asked for and in addition the plate glass clause which, if they had agreed to our proposition in the first instance, would not have been put in. Their trying to force the Limited Company on us has done them no good but made them consent to this Plate Glass Clause. The battle, I believe, is now over and won. Tom was very obstinate but, we believe, made to see that he must give way.

With best love
Your affec. son
(Signed) Richard Pilkington

Figure 7 '… it must be settled …': (cont.)

Windle Will and Rainford Richard are the ones about whom most is known to me. WW and RR were the eldest of six brothers. By family agreement, since there was room for only two in glass, the younger brothers went into coalmining through their mother's family business. This branch of the family also developed Pilkington Tiles and, as a further offshoot, 'Pilkington' or Royal Lancastrian Pottery.

Of the glassmaking Pilkingtons, Windle Will was the 'One'. He was the leader. He was a technical genius, but also an exceptional businessman. He was a tall, handsome man who looked like a king, and behaved like a king. The quality of William is summed up by one of the glassmakers, who said of him: 'Windle can do owt.'

WW was constantly pushing the technology forward. During his watch the following major steps on the road to float glass were introduced:

1. The pot furnaces, where the molten glass was made, became heated by regenerated air, rather than by air at

ambient temperature. The regenerated air gave higher flame temperatures and greater fuel efficiency.

2. At about the same time the pot furnaces gave way to continuous melting in a tank. This produced greater fuel efficiency and more control over the quality of the glass. The development of continuous melting was WW's real claim to fame, and it opened the door to continuous forming and, later, to float.

3. Pilkington started making high-quality plate (or mirror) glass in a brand new works using imported French technology invented by one Bicheroux (Figure 8). Up to this point Pilkington had only manufactured the lower-quality sheet (or window) glass.

Chance Brothers (Pilkington's only rivals by the turn of the century) had tried and failed in the expensive and complex process required to make plate glass, after which Pilkington became the clear leaders. Up to that moment Chance was undoubtedly number one. Its triumph had been the glazing of the Crystal Palace, the centrepiece of the Great Exhibition of 1851.

There is much more to tell about WW (see later), but it is clear that he got on better with his brother than with his cousins. It is evident that he was supported by RR during his heavy spending on new technology. The cousins always tried to put the brakes on.

WW and RR joined forces in 1906 to close a local 'den of iniquity' in St Helens – a theatre (the second Theatre Royal, built in 1862). The brothers were friends of General Booth of the Salvation Army, whose aim was to close every theatre in the country. They bought the theatre and it became the Salvation Army Citadel. A plaque exists to commemorate this event (Plate 5).

Plate 5   Salvation Army plaque

The efforts of William and Richard in attempting to purge the town of its vices were energetic. The post-Georgian era was noted for its licentiousness. Taverns and brothels abounded. Glassmaking was thirsty work, which compounded the problem. It must be remembered that drinking water supplies were often seriously contaminated and uncertain and that beer (much less alcoholic than its modern version) was the healthy drink of choice.

Richard's campaign continued after his death, his will containing a curious clause which attracted the attention of the local newspapers:

> 'My experience has convinced me that the present facilities for the sale of liquors operates to the prejudice of large masses of the community and ought to be curtailed.'

> To this end his Will prohibits any building on his estate to be used for the sale or consumption of intoxicating liquors.

Relatively little is known to me personally about Rainford Richard, even though he was my grandfather. What is known about him is somewhat conjectural. He does not stand out as someone of great attractiveness.

Richard first lived in an old Elizabethan house called Lion House, two miles north-west of St Helens at a place called Crank. In 1874 he bought the house, with 90 acres of land, which had grown to 1,000 acres at the time of his death.

PLATE GLASS - 'BICHEROUX'

POT OF
MOLTEN GLASS

1. A pot of molten glass
is poured out onto
an iron plate to form
a sheet of glass.

2. The glass is
bedded in plaster
by 'dancing' on it.

3. One side of the glass, then the
other, is ground with iron
nogs, sand and water.

4. One side of the glass
is polished with felt
and rouge, then the other.

Figure 8   Plate glass – 'Bicheroux'

Like all those who had 'arrived' socially, he had to build himself a mansion correspondent with his status. He was happy with the site of Lion House, so he decided to construct his mansion with Lion House at its core. The aim of the mansion was to indicate a change in social status from 'trade' to 'upper middle class' and, hopefully, 'county'. (See Jane Austen's writings.) Another way the change in status could be achieved was by genealogy – proving that you were related to the higher classes, if only by royal peccadilloes. (Hence the Pilkington family interest in genealogy, which despite enormous effort never delivered an appropriate result!)

An important social/political event was a visit in 1906 to Rainford Hall by the young Winston Churchill, who spoke at a hustings in support of RR. Winston stayed at Rainford Hall. However, he brought his own bed sheets with him! He took little trouble to disguise from his hosts his feelings of social superiority. As if to emphasise this point, when asked by Richard if he would say goodbye to his wife on departure, Winston replied with words to the effect that that 'wasn't necessary' (Williams-Ellis 1997, p. 82).

Rainford Hall was a fine mansion built in Accrington glazed red-brick complete with a pseudo-Norman entrance hall, with stained glass windows depicting the Pilkingtons' glorious medieval past, three large reception rooms, a billiard room, monogrammed brass door handle plates to the main rooms, 23 bedrooms, and a tiled cellar. The windows were glazed with high-quality, expensive plate glass.

In addition to his partnership in the glassworks, Richard followed his maternal uncle, Joseph Evans, as chairman of the Richard Evans collieries – a very profitable enterprise when coal was 'king'. He was also an alderman and mayor of St Helens, as well as being a colonel in the Volunteers (the Territorial Army of the day). Richard was the commercial strength of Pilkington. He taught his nephew, Austin, all he needed to know. Austin learned the trade thoroughly under the careful direction of Richard. Austin went on to become chairman after his cousin, Arthur, died prematurely soon after the First World War. Austin was complete master of the commercial side of the business in all its aspects (Barker 1977, p. 259).

In 1899 Lord Newton, the retiring Member of Parliament for Newton Division, suggested to Richard that he stand for election to that seat, but that he would not be successful unless he switched from being a Conservative Unionist to being a pure Conservative. This Richard did and he duly won the seat, which he held until the Liberal landslide of 1906. In a word, my grandfather was a VIP.

The election defeat came as a bitter blow to Richard. This, together with another disappointment over a social/military appointment, contributed to his suffering strokes and dying at the comparatively early age of 67 in 1908.

So, what were the conjectural issues which somewhat tarnished his image in my mind? First, the contractors who built Rainford Hall got into financial difficulties and were forced into bankruptcy, after wealthy Richard insisted that they stick to their contract.

Another issue arose in 1907. In those days the military assumed great importance in society's mind, including the civilian element, the Volunteers. Military titles were retained in civvy street. Uniforms were worn for formal occasions such as marriages. Family legend has it that a top position in the Volunteers became vacant, that to Richard's chagrin he did not get this coveted position, and that this was the cause of a stroke which led to his death. The family say that my father, Guy, came home from work at the end of the day to be greeted by his elder brother, Norman, saying: 'The Governor's lost his speech.'

'Oh well, I'm sure we can find it.'

'No! He can't speak!'

This was his first stroke: a second followed soon after which killed him. This incident indicates a serious lack of balance in his character.

Perhaps it was inevitable, now that the family was wealthy, that one member should seek to rise above 'trade'. Ernest, my father's eldest brother, approached his father one fateful day with an outrageous request. 'Governor, settle £20,000 on me. There's room for one gentleman in this family.' Ernest's father-in-law, Baron Schroeder of banking fame, was also reluctantly enrolled in this fundraising scheme. He is said to have uttered 'Mein Gott, it is madness'. Ernest disappeared off a ship in mid-Atlantic in 1932. Nothing more is known about this incident. Was he bored by his life of leisure?

There is strong evidence that Richard was over-committed, particularly when he had Parliamentary duties. His brother, WW, wrote to him requesting him to give him more support and to take his full share in the running of the company. He was described as an industrious MP.

Three years before his death he said in a speech in St Helens 'It has been my lot and my choice to live and work in the neighbourhood in which I was born'. This may give a clue to the Pilkingtons' success – they were not absentee owners. That speech endeared him to me.

Richard had other traits which endeared him to me, even though I never knew him. When he bought his land there was a railway across it with a local station. Richard negotiated with the railway company that they should provide him with one early train a day that would connect with the national network to allow him to go north, south, east or west, and one train later in the day to return him home. The train, as negotiated, continued to run until Beeching axed it in 1964. The endearment was that I lived near this station with my parents and often used the service until I married and flew the nest in 1957.

The other benefit that Grandfather bestowed on my immediate family was his 1,000 acres of land, on which we lived in my youthful years. As children we were allowed to roam 'all over'. If we were challenged by gamekeepers, the password was 'We are Colonel Guy's children'.

Rainford Richard's eldest brother, Windle Will, is the real star of the show. He was a technical genius (with a number of patents to his name), but also a prodigious salesman travelling all over Britain and Europe in search of business (Williams-Ellis 1997, p. 79). Of course, Windle Will and Rainford Richard lived in a simpler age; the company was small, all based in St Helens, there were relatively few employees (approximately 1,500 in 1876), the competitors were falling by the wayside, monopoly was a simple aim for any company, labour was unorganised, government and the Establishment supported enterprise.

Windle Will married Louisa Salter in 1867 and produced four sons and three daughters. Two of his sons, Austin and Cecil, were to lead the company in the third generation. Rainford Richard married Louisa Sinclair in 1868 and produced six sons and two daughters. Three of his sons entered the company, Arthur, Norman and Guy, playing their part but not starring roles.

We have already listed the major forward steps in glassmaking that were taken by WW. As with so much of the company's history, the secret of success always lay in having the best technology.

We also know something of labour relations at that time. One day, as WW walked through the works he saw a man lazing on the railway embankment. A stickler for discipline, he fired him on the spot. Next day, the same man in the same position. WW: 'I thought I told you to get your cards.' 'You did, sir, but I don't work for you, I work for the Railway Company.'

The story is also told of how WW had to battle to get his main claim to fame installed. This was the melting of the glass in a tank

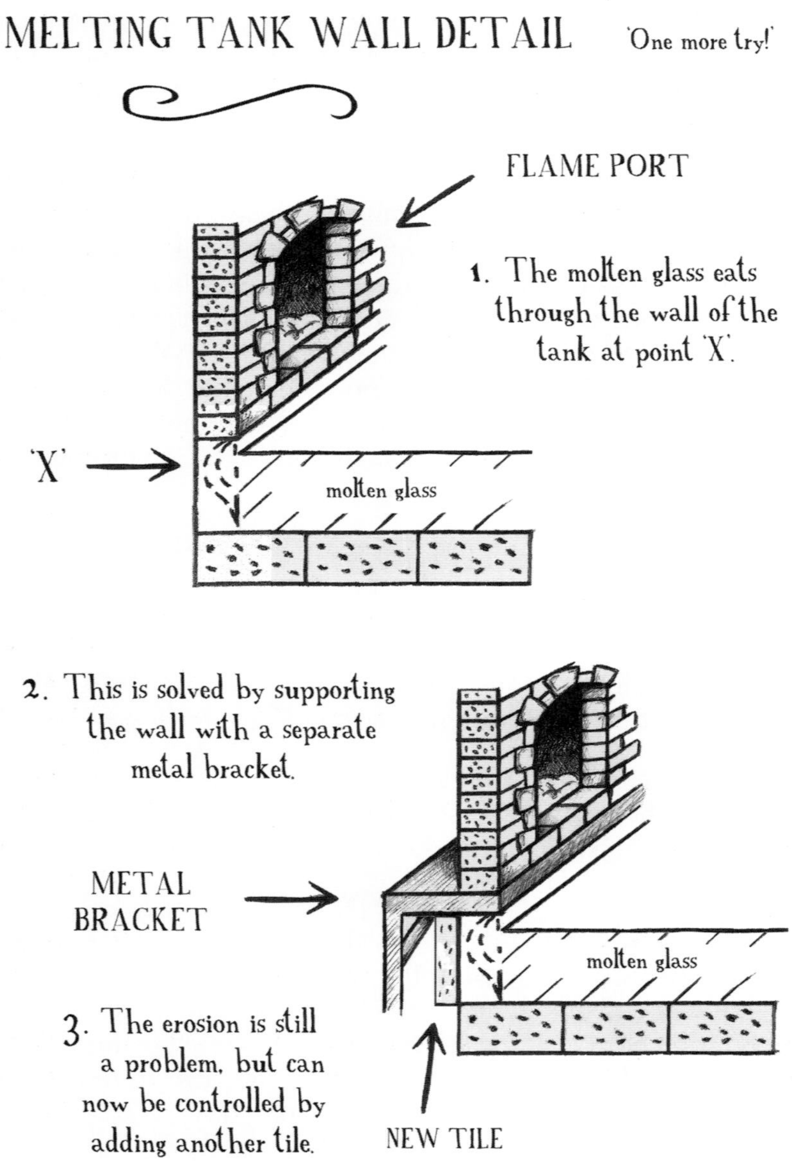

MELTING TANK WALL DETAIL   'One more try!'

FLAME PORT

1. The molten glass eats through the wall of the tank at point 'X'.

'X' →

molten glass

2. This is solved by supporting the wall with a separate metal bracket.

METAL BRACKET →

3. The erosion is still a problem, but can now be controlled by adding another tile.

molten glass

NEW TILE

Figure 9   Melting tank wall detail

rather than a pot. The problem was that WW had constructed the roof of the tank resting on the refractory blocks that enclosed the molten glass. Molten glass is the most corrosive liquid on earth (as seen in the volcanic activity of lava) and it ate away the base of the arch which formed the roof.

After many abortive trials, WW had found the solution – to support the roof on a separate structure, shown in Figure 9. But this needed another trial to prove the point, and more money. The board were itchy (much as happened during the battles to prove float a hundred years later). They were anxious about the mounting cost of WW's experiments.

The board refused WW's request for 'just one more try':

'No, sorry, Will, no more.'

'If that's your answer, I shall take my money and my technology and do it elsewhere!'

'All right, Will, just one more try!'

This time he succeeded and the first major door down that long corridor to float was opened. It was to be forty years before continuous melting was connected to continuous forming (the second major door), and a hundred years before float itself.

Within a short time, WW had about twelve of these tanks on stream. Although they provided continuous melting, the forming of the output into a glass product consisted of about fifteen glass blowers round the 'cold' end, who dipped their blowpipes and gathered the appropriate quantity to form into a cylinder, in effect a continuous offtake.

No drawings exist of these early tanks. WW would just go to a cleared site with the foreman bricklayer and trace the outline of the tank with his foot, plus add a few words about the superstructure and the deed was done. My drawing (Figure 10) is only a guess, but it was likely that the original design would be replicated in the tanks that I knew.

CONTINUOUS MELTING

1. Unmelted batch (sand, soda, and limestone) is tipped on the molten glass.

2. Momentum carries the lumps down the tank ...

3. ... where they are melted by gas flames, and replenish the pool of molten glass.

GAS FLAME PORTS

MOLTEN GLASS

Men gathering molten glass and blowing it into cylinders.

Figure 10   Continuous melting

By the end of the nineteenth century, the powerful flat glass centres in the North East (Hartley) and in Scotland had quickly and completely disappeared. The reasons for their decline are not obvious, but they never made plate glass, probably owing to lack of adequately prepared leadership rather than commercial considerations. Pilkington solved this issue until the third generation, when the same weakness emerged, and nearly prevailed. (See Chapter 5, 'The Third Generation'.)

The power of the great industrial dynasties (Rowntree, Lever, Cadbury) had not yet declined. The glue of Nonconformism (Quaker and Congregationalist) gave those involved in such enterprises an advantage. They were working for something bigger than themselves. The name I have given to this glue in Pilkington is 'the Soul of Pilkington', and it is hinted at throughout the book. Monopoly in business was still accepted in the UK, which gave a simple aim to any potentially up-and-coming business, and it was certainly in the Pilkington sights.

After long struggles for success, there occurred a golden period in the time of the second generation, towards the end of the nineteenth century, when large profits were being made, and special bonuses were paid to the partners. The reason for this could be summed up as the successful incorporation of the manufacture of plate glass into the Pilkington portfolio.

This golden period in the company's history was accompanied by serious trouble with labour (as was also experienced in Sir Harry's reign exactly 100 years later, in 1970). There was a strike of the glassworkers in 1870 in Sheet Works (the only works). The issue was over a wage reduction required by the 'masters' to combat growing Belgian imports. The 'servants' (there were no effective trade unions) walked out, but came back unconditionally on the 'masters'' terms six months and two weeks later, a very different scenario from what happened 100 years later in 1970. (See Chapter 12, 'Rebellion: The 1970 Strike'.)

The person who met the various works' deputations during this time was always the masterful Windle Will. In 1890, twenty years later, there was a strike at the new Plate Works. Again the issue was wages, the 'servants' requesting a wage increase. This time there was trade union backing (the United Plate Glass Workers), but to no avail. The 'servants' came back unconditionally on the 'masters" terms four months and two weeks later, Windle Will once again in charge and successful.

Of course, as noted above, socialism was emerging as a new force. The Chartist movement grew in the middle of the nineteenth century, demanding in its charter many of the elements we now accept as normal in our present democracy. It was regarded by the 'masters' as unacceptable – revolutionary. The Chartist movement was put down bloodlessly. A Parliamentary Act was promulgated, called the Reform Act, but it was a pale shadow of what the Chartists had demanded.

In order to achieve what they did, the second generation of the Pilkingtons had to be as much pioneers, risking all, as their forebears. Competition was as powerful as ever. Even though their rivals were falling by the wayside, their competitors who survived were also growing stronger. In the end, there was only Chance Brothers (Birmingham). Chance Brothers was finally taken over in 1951.

So the 'Four' dwindled over 25 years to the 'Two' – Windle Will and his brother, Rainford Richard. Richard became more involved in external affairs, becoming an MP in 1899, leaving the 'One', Windle Will, standing out in stark relief as leader of the Glass Act. It was Windle Will's children, Austin and Cecil, who were to rule the next generation, and Windle Will's grandchild, Sir Harry, who was to rule the next generation after that (the fourth). This line of the family shows most clearly how the Soul of Pilkington developed, in terms of its people taking long-term views, caring for each other, embracing best technology, and ploughing back the profits.

Chapter Four

Moon on Pond (Fantasy Number 2)

A fantasy about the second generation of the Pilkingtons.

(*Fantasy in italics*. Reality in roman.)

William Pilkington (Windle Will) is talking to his younger brother, Richard (Rainford Richard), my grandfather.

'Richard, I've just been mesmerised.'

'You look excited, Will. What's happened?'

'Well, you know how I like to walk home from work most nights. That's what I have just done. Something happened to me tonight, almost like a vision. As I passed by the new pond we've just had made, the harvest moon caught my eye. You know how large it looks, and tonight it was, in addition, a glorious yellow pink. That was striking enough, but the magic moment was seeing its reflection on the pond's surface. Somehow, I was transfixed. There was not a breath of wind. The image was perfect.'

'Go on.'

'It wasn't just the beauty of the scene that captured me. Something even more powerful came to me. Here was what we have been looking for – the perfect mirror. This is how to do it, using the perfect flatness and brightness of a liquid.'

'I don't understand. Are you saying that we can capture such a perfect image as that in a piece of glass?'

'Yes, why not? Somehow we must learn how to do just that!'

'But, what's wrong with our present mirrors? I know that sometimes there is residual distortion and sometimes the grinding pits are not polished out.'

'I'll tell you what's wrong with them. All that you've mentioned and they are excessively expensive, so very little is sold, and in small sizes and small quantities.'

'I can see that the quality could be better, but why should they be cheaper?'

'Obvious! No expensive machinery for grinding and polishing, far fewer workmen, less electricity, no need to buy the sand for grinding, no rouge for polishing – just floating glass on a liquid metal. And, listen to this, if it worked, all flat glass could be made by the same process!'

'My God, Will, you are in cloud-cuckoo-land!'

'But think of it, Richard! We'd rule the world!'

'The idea is far too revolutionary. Our partners would never countenance the cost of that kind of experiment. You know how they tend to block all progress if a lot of money is involved.'

'William and Thomas – we don't need to tell them. I will do a few simple tests in the lab and then we will take out a patent to protect the idea. That will cost very little. They can't object to that.'

The two brothers were right to be a little chary of their cousins. The memory was fresh of how, only ten years ago, the same cousins had tried to bring outside shareholders in so as to dilute the capital and allow higher dividends to be distributed.

A few weeks later, the brothers' conversation resumed.

'It's no good. I can't get it to work. The technical problems are overwhelming.'

William was unusually quiet, he was crestfallen.

'Tell me, Will' (his brother was upset to see his elder brother like this), 'what's happened?'

'Oh, Richard, I'm so disappointed. The concept is brilliant, but the practice is impossible. We know from our basic knowledge of science that pure metals do not react with molten glass. Do you remember that gold sovereign we dropped into the pot? Later we found it, melted, but otherwise unchanged. So the basic concept is fine.

'I took a little feed off our new continuous melter and poured it into a small refractory box onto molten lead as the carrier – the lead just went up in smoke. It is so volatile at that temperature, and poisonous.

'I tried tin instead of lead. That was better, but the tin still oxidised and coated the inside of the box with tin oxide. Tin oxide fell onto the top surface. The bottom surface was also spoiled with something, probably tin oxide.

'The process will have to be continuous, and I cannot see how to get the molten glass onto the tin and off the tin and keep the oxygen out. We would have to buy vast numbers of flasks of nitrogen, and probably hydrogen, in order to protect the tin surface. That cost alone rules the process out. Perhaps one day we could buy a continuous economical supply of these gasses, but nobody is able to provide such a thing now.'

'Did the others see you?'

'Yes, Thomas did, but I think I fobbed him off.'

'How did you do that?'

'Because there is a halfway stage to the Holy Grail, and that is to make a continuous sheet, or ribbon, of glass blanks, not fire-finished, but rough caste, suitable to be put under our existing grinders and polishers. We know how to melt continuously and I'm sure we could learn to pour the molten glass through water-cooled rollers to make rough caste continuously. So I fobbed him off with that kind of talk.'

'But, we would also need to learn how to anneal a continuous ribbon. We know something about annealing single sheets on a continuous basis but not a ribbon.'

'Much work to be done and much persuasion of our cousins.'

End of Fantasy. The 'Four' never did achieve any of the above ideas, but there was no reason to suppose that they did not dream them. The fact is that some American glassmakers did dream, and published some patents in the early nineteen-hundreds, which described the float process very accurately (Appendix 4). The Americans could dream it up, but they wouldn't have been able to do it for the reasons narrated above.

Those American patents stood in Alastair's way 50 years later. Eventually, he and his team found a way through them to create an even stronger patent position. After all, the Americans had only dreamed. Alastair did it!

Chapter Five

The Third Generation – Nearly Lost It (1894–1931)

The third generation is in many ways the most interesting. The company seemed to be in perpetual crisis during their tenure. They made a number of serious business mistakes. They nearly drove the company into bankruptcy. Their tenure ended with the 'Big Row'. These elements will all be covered in some detail in this and the next chapter.

The third generation of the family gets a bad press. Elizabeth Williams-Ellis writes of 'clogs to clogs in three generations'. Theo Barker is not complimentary about this generation either, but he does point out that whatever their shortcomings this generation suffered much ill luck, as will be seen later in this chapter.

Moreover, there is a lot of credit to be given to the third generation. They faced huge problems:

1. They had to weather the cataclysm of the First World War and particularly its effect on the labour movement, with so many men killed, including many factory workers, and many of the future managerial class wiped out. The lack of workers increased militancy and trade union power, which culminated in the General Strike of 1925 and the miners' strike of 1926. Pilkington reacted positively to the emergence of organised labour by setting up a formal method of

dealing with labour issues – a Joint Industrial Council for wage negotiations. In addition, properly funded and jointly managed pension schemes, providing pensions for all, were established. It was this generation that established Pilkington as a caring company.

2.   The partners also had to face big changes in glassmaking, both in sheet and plate, immediately after the War. The changes could not have been more fundamental. They were from intermittent manual methods to continuous mechanised manufacture. In addition to meeting the technical demands of taming these new methods, they built an expensive new works to make plate glass on the east coast, at Doncaster. Barker says this was a mistake – the decision-making was faulty. Doncaster was unnecessary.

3.   The third major problem was the raising of finance to pay for the manufacturing changes mentioned above and, also, the cost of dealing with the pains of surplus labour, including retraining.

The company was too small to take on such financial burdens. It was forced to arrange loans from the Bank of England and the Prudential. The partners had to dip into their pockets. These burdens were so great that they prevented the technical progress which was required in the glassmaking.

But there was something even more serious and fundamental happening in the company. The partners could not cope any more. Worse still, they did not realise that they were not coping. The company was suffering from an out-of-date organisation. Everybody had a finger in every pie. There were no clear lines of responsibility. There was no delegation of authority. The managers – so-called – could not take decisions and had to refer everything to higher authority.

It wasn't that the partners were lazy or incompetent – it was more to do with the fact that the company had grown beyond a partnership but still had the management style of a partnership. The company needed a new cohesive force. The old glue of common blood and adherence to strong moral principles was no longer enough. What was needed was the cohesive force of a proper and effective company organisation.

As with the previous generation, there were two key family members who ran the company. (See Plate 6 for portraits of the major players of the third generation.) They were brothers, Austin and Cecil, both children of the star of the previous generation – Windle Will. They were both great men in their own way, and their greatness showed in the final act of the third generation, when they accepted with good grace that they were 'fired'. They were below the accepted retirement age – Austin 60 and Cecil 56 at that time – so there was no apparent need to retire except that they both stood in the way of progress.

Once the Great War was over, the company had to face the major glassmaking upheavals mentioned at the beginning of this chapter. One decision they got wrong, one decision they got right.

There were two quite different methods of making flat glass at that time. The two methods were called 'sheet' and 'plate'. The sheet process made low-quality glass, suitable for house windows. The plate process made high-quality, suitable for mirrors and large shop windows. The decision they got wrong was the manufacture of sheet; the decision they got right was the manufacture of plate.

It will be recalled that sheet, from time immemorial, had been made with a blowpipe (Figure 3). A gob of molten glass on the end of a blowpipe was first blown into a bubble. The bubble was converted into a flat disc by spinning to yield small panes of glass. Although a glassblower could make a disc 6' in diameter, the maximum size of pane available was small, about 36'6" x 24'4".

Soon it was realised that the bubble could be elongated into a cylinder by dangling the bubble over a pit. The cylinder yielded much bigger panes of glass but the cylinder then had to be cut and flattened (Figure 5). The flattening added new faults, but the glass was good enough for windows and cheaper than crown, so the ancient crown process was finally abandoned. But the company stuck by the cylinder process for far too long (see later in the chapter), long after much truer ways of making flat glass had emerged.

The partners dithered over what to do in sheet. There was good reason for the uncertainty. They were faced with a choice between systems. There was cylinder drawn, an established, reliable process, if illogical in the sense that we were not making glass cylinders! Although the company used it for a few years, it had to be a dead duck.

There existed two competing commercially successful methods of making the glass the way you wanted it – flat! – with a generic name, 'flat drawn'. Both were inconsistent as to the quality of the product and the stability of the forming method. Their names were Fourcault and Colburn. It required the company to make up its mind at an early stage which one to back. Because they dithered, other glassmakers got in early and took licences.

This dithering was partly due to Cecil. Being a perfectionist, as well as an extremely competent glass technologist, he knew that there was a better method not yet invented. Cecil told me that he was on the threshold of what turned out to be the successful PPG process (Appendix 3). He had a full-scale experimental unit to work with. Unfortunately his experimental work was stopped by the miners' strike (1925–6), when *all* production was forced to stop owing to lack of fuel. When production resumed after the eighteen-month strike, the board refused any further costly

Directors
1. Mr. Richard Austin Pilkington (Chairman)
2. Mr. Alfred Cecil Pilkington
3. Col. William Norman Pilkington
4. The Lord Cozens-Hardy
5. Major Guy Reginald Pilkington
6. Major Geoffrey Langton Pilkington

Plate 6   The third generation

experimental work. This was a major error on the partners' part. If the chairman, Austin, had backed Cecil like Sir Harry backed Alastair, they would have got the best process in 1926, before PPG, and Pilkington would have led the world in sheet glass.

Manufacture of plate carried on in parallel, and the upheaval which Pilkington got right was the change in the manufacture of plate. The plate process was costly and complex compared to the blowpipe. The plate process was a technological development (developed by the French) dating from the sixteenth century. It consisted of making a large blank by pouring molten glass from a pot through rollers onto a flat table. These blanks had rough surfaces which had to be ground flat and polished to transparency. The grinding was done by cast iron and sand, the polishing by felt and rouge. Space had to be made available within the works perimeter for the waste products of the process – the glass ground off, and the used sand and rouge.

The quality of the end product for mirrors and large windows may have been adequate but the cost of getting there was high. The capital cost of building a plate works was immense. An army of workers was required to operate the complex processes.

It may also be recalled from Chapter 3 that Pilkington had learned how to melt glass continuously, but nowhere in the company (or indeed the world) had molten glass been turned into a continuous ribbon of flat glass. The melting might be continuous, but the forming wasn't. And, in plate glass, the situation was further behind. Even in Pilkington, where continuous melting was known, it had not been used for plate manufacture.

This was a lapse in thinking on the part of the company. To have invented continuous melting in 1880 (as Windle Will had done in the previous generation), and not to have followed it up quickly by continuous forming, needs some explanation. This lapse in thinking is what happens when there is a lack of proper leadership.

Sheet was made in one works called 'Sheet Works', and plate was made in another works one mile distant, in a separate facility called 'Plate Works'. Each location had its own culture and each rather disparaged the other. (In Plate Works the managers wore hats, in Sheet Works they were bareheaded!)

In Sheet Works the continuous melters were connected to a virtual form of continuous forming by having a number of glass blowers at the cold end leading their blowpipes one after the other. Two embryonic ways of forming a flat fire-finished sheet straight from the melting had been invented by competitors. The glass was of doubtful quality but nevertheless should have been followed up vigorously by Pilkington.

In plate, the situation was different. There were no continuous melters in Plate Works, but they had the answer to continuous forming. Blanks ready for grinding and polishing were made by the Bicheroux process. In this process one pot of molten glass is poured between rollers (like a giant mangle) to make one blank. It was surely an obvious next step to connect these rollers to a continuous feed off a continuous melter and so cast a continuous ribbon.

So slow were Pilkington in their technical progress that the answer was provided by someone quite other who had the required foresight and vigour, Henry Ford. Enter the Ford Motor Company! The improbable story of how a motor car manufacturer became a key player in the manufacture of plate (and unwittingly opened the way to float) is not only worth telling, it is vital to our story. The date is 1920.

Henry Ford had only one child, a son called Edsel, tutored rather than schooled, by a man named Avery. Satisfied that he could teach Edsel no more, Avery presented himself to Henry. Instead of paying him off, Henry told him to look round the factory to see if there was any improvement that could be made. If Avery's brief was vague, his reply to Henry was clear: 'Why don't we make windscreens?' And Henry's response was even clearer: 'Do it!'

After a big struggle Avery had moved a long way forward, to the point where his pilot plant could make a continuous ribbon, eighteen inches wide – the width of a windscreen (narrow compared to the normal plate dimensions). He found that making glass was not that easy, and after struggling for over a year Ford invited the plate glass makers of Europe and the USA to help.

The other plate makers turned their noses up at Ford's efforts, partly because of blindness to the significance of Ford's invention and partly because they didn't want to establish another competitor. The Pilkington team contained someone who was familiar with continuous melting and saw that Ford's attempts at continuous forming exactly fitted the bill. Cecil Pilkington embraced the idea. He saw that Ford had solved the basics. A deal was arranged, and within a short time a 60'0" wide ribbon of glass had been made in St Helens, to be cut into blanks ready for grinding and polishing.

A celebration dinner was arranged at Ford at which Cecil Pilkington was the guest of honour. Mrs Avery was placed next to Cecil, who told me that she wearied him with endless questions about the King of England (George V). What use was he, and why didn't the English have a president like the USA? Cecil stood up and proclaimed: 'At this point in England we have a custom. I give you the loyal toast – ladies and gentlemen, the King.' Afterwards some Ford people came to Cecil: 'You sure fixed that gal!'

There was now continuous melting and continuous casting of a ribbon of blanks for plate. What was needed was a way of grinding and polishing the blanks continuously. Pilkington did just that (Figure 11). They now led the world in the manufacture of high-quality plate and kept that lead until float took over 30 years later.

This lead position in plate imposed great financial strains on the company. It appeared then to require the building of a second plate glass works on the east coast at Doncaster as a response to increasing demand for plate and as a deterrent to continental competitors nosing around the British market. (Theo Barker's view, however, was that the building of Doncaster was a mistake, that it was not necessary.) In addition to building Doncaster they had to rearrange the existing plate glass works in St Helens.

They had taken the right technical decision on plate. They stuck to the rapidly developing plate process, and it was to carry them through the failure of the sheet process.

Let us return to sheet and the decision they got wrong. There were now three ways to go for the world's sheet glass makers:

1. License one of the existing embryonic flat drawn methods, Fourcault or Colburn (Appendix 3), developed during the First World War and producing saleable, if questionable, quality.

2. Invent a new process, the obvious process of drawing a flat sheet straight from the molten glass (e.g. dipping a knife in treacle with no interference).

3. Develop the cylinder principle to its ultimate by drawing a cylinder instead of blowing. (See Figure 12 for a description of 'cylinder drawn'.)

The dilemma was, which one to back? Pilkington went for cylinder drawn. They should have gone for licensing one of the existing methods of drawing a flat ribbon, but at the same time financing Cecil to develop (2). They stuck with the 'cylinder' principle – bravely, but wrongly.

My sister, Elisabeth, is one of the few people alive as I write these words who saw cylinder drawn in the late 1920s. Her father (Guy) took her into Sheet Works and the sight of this extraordinary process clearly made an impact on her senses:

PLATE GLASS – CONTINUOUS

1. Molten glass from the tank is fed through rollers.

2. The ribbon of glass is cut into rectangular sheets.

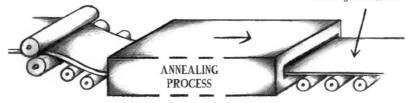

ANNEALING PROCESS

3. The plates are taken down a continuous table under a series of grinding heads where one side is ground smooth, then brought back, turned over, and taken down again to grind the other side.

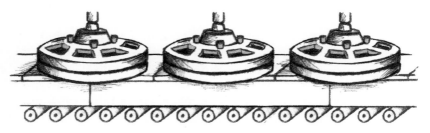

4. The same process is repeated but this time using polishing heads rather than grinding heads.

Figure 11   Plate glass – continuous

We walked into this dark space lit by the flares of great furnaces. It was a huge space of great height. It was a terribly hot, vast cathedral-like place. The men in cloth caps were all working in groups and the floor was covered in small bits of broken glass. There were two, maybe three, columns of glass cylinders being drawn up from each place, a sort of pool for each cylinder each full of white hot liquid glass. The head of each cylinder looked as if it had been lowered into each of the white hot pools and was being so slowly drawn up that they were scarcely moving. Each cylinder was at a different height, different stages in the drawing up.

There was noise, the noise of great machinery in action, the men shouting. Each cylinder glowed, beautiful, transparent and pink. The diameter of the cylinders must have been, my memory says, about three to four feet across.

One of the cylinders had been drawn up to the ceiling height of this hugely hot place. With a team of men all moving very precisely, slowly the cylinder became lowered onto cradle-like trucks all lined up to have the cylinder resting where it could be cut into lengths. The length of each cut cylinder makes me think of the length of large motor cars of my youth. The glass cylinder still glowed pinkish and transparent.

I remember being conscious of how dangerous it was to bring these great glass cylinders down to the cradle trucks among the unprotected workmen. Later I heard the works always had a surgeon on duty.

Father told me that these cut up cylinders had to be taken to where they were flattened.

Of cylinder drawn it might be said: 'It's magnificent, but it's not glassmaking.' Cecil, the technical leader, knew in his heart that it was not the way forward. By what stretch of the imagination could it be right, when making a flat pane of glass, to first make

CYLINDER DRAWN

1. A circular metal 'bait' is dipped into a pot of molten glass.

2. The bait is then raised into the air, pulling the molten glass with it.

3. As the glass is pulled out of the pot it cools slightly, stiffening and forming the walls of a growing cylinder.

4. Compressed air is blown down the centre of the cylinder to keep its shape.

5. The completed cylinder is now swung down to the floor for cutting and flattening.

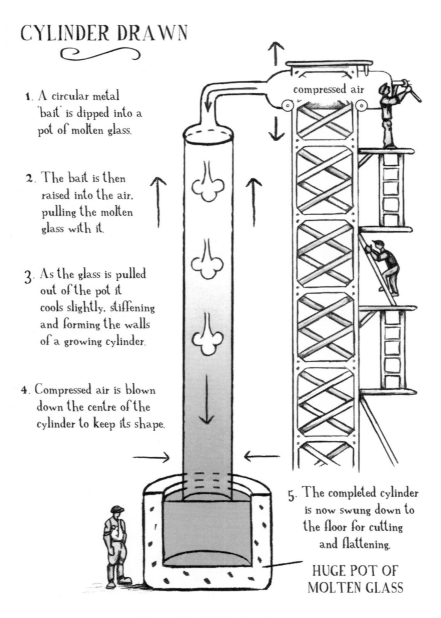

compressed air

HUGE POT OF MOLTEN GLASS

Figure 12   Cylinder drawn

it the wrong shape – a cylinder! Particularly when there existed two embryonic flat drawn methods. Cecil, no doubt, had dipped his knife in treacle and lifted it out, thus forming a flat curtain for a moment. Why could he not do the same with molten glass? As with treacle, so with molten glass. The problem was the edges. The edges waisted in. Surface tension effects continued to pull the edges inwards as the sheet continued to pull up, finishing up with nothing but a thread.

Fourcault and Colburn had solved the problem of the waisting edges, but at the expense of distortion and surface quality (Appendix 3). The products were undoubtedly cheaper and therefore commercially more attractive than cylinder drawn. Cecil's only dilemma should have been which of the two processes to back, but Cecil was a purist. He could see that a better flat drawn process could potentially exist. He was sure he could find it. And there were difficulties in obtaining a licence for the other flat drawn processes.

Cecil told me that he was on the verge of solving the edge problem on a full-scale pilot plant but was stopped by the miners' strike of 1926, which not only stopped the pilot plant but all production on glass for many months. Following the restoration of coal supplies glassmaking resumed, but Cecil was prevented by the board from experimenting further. The failure to back Cecil was a major mistake. If the board had backed him, as they backed Alastair 35 years later, Pilkington would have become number one so much earlier and would not have had to become a public company so soon. Cecil did not have the clout that his grandfather Windle Will had to get his own way.

It was an American glassmaker, Pittsburgh Plate Glass (PPG), which solved the edge problem, with such an utterly simple idea that Cecil must have kicked himself. For eager beavers the technical mysteries of the flat drawn processes are made transparent in Appendix 3.

The PPG process, as it was later developed, was good enough to become a challenge to float.

Cecil (Alfred Cecil Pilkington) was wonderfully dedicated to technology. He told me that he introduced a pyrometer into a kiln in order to measure the temperature which up to that point had been measured 'by the eye' of the operator. A harbinger of things to come in 1920. The operator in charge asked, 'What's that for?' Cecil explained. The operator replied, 'If that stays, I'm going.' And he did. This incident illustrates the difficulty of introducing new technology, especially in the earliest days.

Cecil slept in the works on occasion. He told me himself, 'Cousin Herbert used to send his carriage to take me home. So kind.' His son, Arnold, wrote to me in a letter dated 1983 about 'the glass-making tanks' with which he (Cecil) was so obsessed. Cecil would sit on a chair alongside a tank, lost in observation. My father remembered visiting the works and enquiring of a glassmaker how things were going, who replied, 'T'wurr all reet, 'til that there h'Alfred came and made a bugger of it.'

Cecil appears to have been quite free of 'extramural' activities. He had the Pilkington hobby – gardening. He had a special fruit tree onto which were grafted six different species of apple. After retirement he focused his technical abilities on farming. In his youth he had made a balloon out of silk which he had filled with hydrogen (of his own making). The balloon was flown, and up the tether went a rocket which ignited a spectacular explosion over the heads of a surprised local populace.

My father thought Cecil was mad. He certainly was mad in the sense of being totally focused on glassmaking, to the exclusion of any other aspects of the business. 'Unbalanced' is a better word.

George McOnie, one of the first graduates to be recruited, told me that he was requested to attend St Helens for interview with Cecil. He arrived from Scotland on a Friday (the date is 1929) only to be told to come back on Monday. Cecil was missing. Much fluttering in the dovecots. Cecil was finally tracked down. He had forgotten and was 83 miles away in Doncaster! George did come back, was taken on and rose to be a member of the board.

The board tried to curtail Cecil's excesses. Percy Truesdale (one of Cecil's men) told me that he was summoned in front of the whole board, which included Cecil, who were sitting in the full formality of the boardroom. Austin in the chair! There, he was told that he was not to work any longer with Cecil on the window glass process at Sheet Works. Every other member of the team was similarly and individually instructed.

After the board meeting, Cecil searched out Percy. 'Sorry you had to hear all that, Truesdale, but the chairman said nothing about Ravenhead Works, did he? Right, see you there this afternoon!'

Cecil's brilliance in glass technology was matched similarly by Austin's brilliance on the sales side. Austin had a detailed grasp and knowledge of the customers, in addition to extremely good personal relationships with them. All Pilkington sales were to glass merchants. It was the glass merchants who stocked glass and dealt with the ultimate users. Austin knew them all.

Cecil was a warm, very likeable character. Austin was more austere, but was noted for kindness and acts of generosity. Austin was unable to delegate any of his work. It was said that a queue of managers assembled daily outside Austin's office door seeking his decisions. Some were reputed to attend with a spurious request, simply to be 'seen'.

Austin had another element of unbalance. He spent much time and energy outside Pilkington (national treasurer of the YMCA, active member of the London Missionary Society, unelected honorary chairman of the St Helens Local Authority Education Committee). Such was his public prominence, it is said he was offered a knighthood, which he turned down (out of a false sense of humility?).

As we have seen, the earlier generations of the family demonstrated a rather rigid attitude to their workers (no doubt typical of the age before organised labour). It was the third generation who developed the reputation of Pilkington Brothers as a caring company.

It could be argued that the Pilkingtons had no choice but to become more humane if they were to keep their plants running, but they did more than was required for that objective. They had, in 1847, set up a recreation club (the first in the country) for cricket and bowls. There were welfare officers in their works later in the nineteenth century, followed by medical facilities.

During the First World War so many men were killed on the Western Front that there was a shortage of labour. An initiative taken by a London borstal (and organised by my father) was to send suitable boys up to St Helens to be apprenticed to glassmaking. The presence of a hostel and training school for orphans was general knowledge. The origin of a portion of the pupils was secret and remained a secret. The cover was that they were Boy Scouts. My father had a Scouter's uniform, but never wore it! As chairman of the St Helens Scout Association he visited jamborees in the south (no doubt making some selection). It was a case of company enlightened self-interest.

Cecil and Austin, the leaders of the third generation, donated some of their personal fortunes to a Trust Fund to help their workers displaced by the major step of continuous mechanised glassmaking. These donations, together with other family, and some company, input, are the foundations of the present welfare organisation which provides benefits to Pilkington pensioners and widows.

Austin and Cecil's capital fund has now (2010) grown to £70 million and provides the fund with £2 million per annum to spend on the pensioners and widows. The benefits provided change and develop from time to time, depending on company and external circumstances. Originally there were coal gifts, seed gifts, monetary gifts to those in need. Another early initiative (1936) was the provision of family allowances to assist those with more than one child, well before the welfare state took over. All these have been superseded.

The original assistance to displaced workers is still there, but has been taken over by the formal wage negotiation bodies, with the trade unions. The pensions, no longer at the partners' whim, are provided by separate funds under the control of trustee bodies which have equal representation from the company and the beneficiaries, as well as joint funding.

Today the Trust Fund aims its resources towards the more needy pensioners and widows, mainly through care in the home – subsidised meals on wheels, draught proofing, security – and other home-based services. There is a whole system of welfare visiting to ensure that the needs of pensioners and their dependants are being met. There is a separate residential respite care home, Ruskin Lodge. This also provides a centre for socialising during the day.

The establishment of the Pilkingtons as a caring company must remain as the third generation's claim to fame. It might be argued 'clogs to clogs' occurred because there was overemphasis on the human at the expense of the efficient. One of my aims in writing this book is to refute that argument and to demonstrate that humanity and efficiency support each other.

As will be seen in the chapter on the fourth generation, the development of labour relations had to be taken further. The wake-up call came in 1970 when all the glassworkers walked out and put a complete stop to production for seven weeks. The human systems introduced by the third generation were not robust enough and major improvements were forced on the fourth.

So now we are ready to say goodbye to the third generation and step into the fourth. Unlike the smooth handing over of batons by the first generation to the second, and by the second to the third, the transition from the third to the fourth generation was messy, multifaceted, but, above all, dramatic. The drama centred on an incident known in family folklore as the 'Big Row'.

Those who really knew what happened, and exactly what the 'Big Row' was about, went to the grave without revealing that knowledge. The row was between Austin and Cecil. The fact that nobody 'talked' simply added fuel to the fire and makes anybody who is interested in the incident even keener to find out.

Theo Barker, who as the official company historian needed to know about this seminal moment, was left in the dark. I beseeched one of those who knew (Lawrence, second son of Austin) to talk to Barker. Lawrence said to me, 'No, we don't want to raise all that tittle-tattle.'

My attempt at understanding the 'Big Row' in detail is contained in the next chapter. Whatever the rights and wrongs of the situation, it precipitated the departure of two key people who ran the company.

The many aspects of the multifaceted transition have already been covered. The company organisation was creaking, the top held all the reins, they persisted with an out-of-date glassmaking technology, the company accounts showed a half-year loss. The company was facing bankruptcy.

The saving grace of the situation was that they had in their midst someone who could see clearly what was needed, Edward Cozens-Hardy. His strength was a clear mind, an overall view, a grasp of the finances. Unlike Austin and Cecil, he was not a specialist. He had been a director for twenty years. His sister had married Austin.

Circumstances and Cozens-Hardy forced the issue, and in ways that remain tantalisingly uncharted, the third generation was replaced by the fourth. As the midwife who oversaw the strange birth of the fourth, this Cozens-Hardy deserves a chapter to himself, Chapter 7, which I have called 'The Cozens-Hardy Era'.

Chapter Six

The Big Row: Schism at the Top

The major confrontation, known in family folklore as the 'Big Row', took place in 1931. It was between the two Pilkington brothers who more or less ran the company. Austin, the elder, was chairman. His skill was in the commercial field. Cecil, four years younger, was the technical wizard.

It was well-known that Austin and Cecil did not get on with each other. Arnold Pilkington, Cecil's son (who did not join the company), wrote to me in 1983: 'I know he [Cecil] never got on particularly well with Uncle Austin, but that is presently generally known.'

Theo Barker (1977) reports that there 'was a confrontation in the directors' luncheon room at the end of June [1931] when Austin Pilkington had words with his brother Cecil. (According to Lord Pilkington, Cozens-Hardy seized the opportunity to slip out in order to avoid having to take sides.)' (p. 324).

Things were coming to a head on a number of fronts. Only a month before, on 22 May, the board had had to make the decision that the half-year dividend would be withheld. It was known that Chance Brothers, their only British rival, was at the same time distributing substantial dividends. There were plenty of reasons, why some plain speaking between the key partners was becoming necessary.

The issue which triggered the open rift between the brothers concerned Weeks (Ronald Morce Weeks). Weeks was a family member who had been appointed to the board as a full director in 1928, three years before the Row. He was a very competent man, educated at Cambridge, where he had achieved a Blue as captain of the university football eleven. Highly recommended by the University, he had been taken on straight from there to work in Plate Works. He rose rapidly to become works manager.

The reason Weeks was a family member was that in 1921 he had married Elsie Haynes, a great-granddaughter of one of the original Pilkington brothers ('Go-getter' William). Unfortunately, Elsie suffered mental trouble and became confined to a mental home. In those days such mental problems were allowed as a cause for divorce.

Weeks successfully sued for divorce and married again in 1931. Austin baulked; Cecil accepted. The evidence points beyond reasonable doubt to Weeks' divorce being the trigger for the Big Row.

In a letter to Elizabeth Williams-Ellis, Roger Pilkington (Sir Harry's younger brother) states:

> As manager of the Cowley Hill plant, Weeks was an important man.
>
> My father (Austin) was chairman at the time, and he took the view that 'for richer, for poorer, in sickness or in health' was what one had openly promised. Whatever the law of the land said was irrelevant. Ronnie Weeks had to go, he said.
>
> On the other side was my uncle Cecil, who championed the legal right of Weeks to get rid of his wife and remarry. The quarrel between the two brothers was a very bitter one. Cecil had no church leanings, I think; and the result was that my father resigned from the Chairmanship.

Austin's strong views on sexual conduct received confirmation in an audiotape sent by Roger Pilkington to Isabel Henniger,

Lawrence's daughter. Roger's tape relates an incident when Austin was a St Helens town councillor (as well as chairman of Pilkington). A fellow councillor had been caught by a police raid in a brothel in Liverpool. (Family memory recalls that the councillor was having sex with a sailor.) Austin used a lawyer to force the Town Clerk to put a motion about dismissing the councillor from the Council. The Town Clerk did not want to do it, but because of the legal pressure the motion was put and carried.

With this background, we may infer that Austin may have felt that Weeks was not a suitable person to be a director of Pilkington and talked to Cecil in these terms. It is easy to imagine Cecil's reaction.

In Weeks, Cecil could see he had a ready-made successor. Already Cecil was being drawn away from St Helens owing to his wife's health and was working part-time, spending much time in Oxford where he had built a brand new sound-proofed house. A gap in the top management was yawning. And on top of that, here was Austin proposing to blow a hole below the waterline. Austin's sales teams were totally dependent on the glass technology. It was glass quality and cost which sold the product – not salesmanship. There was nobody else in the same frame technically as Ronald Weeks.

We can see now why such a religio-sexual issue was so powerful and so sensitive that later generations did not want to talk about it. In 1920 one of the sons, Charles, of Col. Richard Pilkington of Rainford Hall (Rainford Richard) divorced, which proved greatly upsetting to the family.

Later generations would also be sensitive to the fact that, apart from the Row, Austin and Cecil had been running the company into bankruptcy (Barker 1977). With such fault lines in the third generation, it was clearly time for them to move over and let in the fourth. Before the fourth generation are in position to take over, we need to hear how Cozens-Hardy took things in hand and reorganised the company in preparation for Sir Harry's chairmanship of the fourth generation and the dawning of a golden age.

Chapter Seven

The Cozens-Hardy Era:
The Rescue of the Glass Act
by an In-Law (1931–1945)

The Glass Act had faltered. The qualifications for family directors had been diluted. Membership of the family had become more important than capability.

The fourth generation had a strange birth, the 'beheading of the King' – the firing of Austin Pilkington and his brother, Cecil, the leaders of the third generation. The catalyst for this revolutionary act was Edward Cozens-Hardy, Third Baron. Like Cromwell, he became the Protector rather than claiming the crown.

Who was this Edward Cozens-Hardy (C-H) who had married into the Pilkingtons? Could he have effected an all-out takeover? His family were not wealthy but were not poor. He had connections. He had charisma. He could easily have persuaded some of the existing shareholding family members (these totalled only 50) to fall in behind him. He'd been around a long time. He had been a full director since 1908. His sister, Hope, had married Austin (not yet chairman). He had a son (Peter) in the business. C-H was in his prime at the time of the beheading, still only 58.

He must have been tempted to become King, to make a full-blown takeover bid. Why didn't he do it? There was no individual left who had the power that C-H had at this moment in the company's history. He was unquestionably the boss.

There were obviously parts of the family who might well have felt resentment towards him over the reorganisation, and who would have resisted him. My mother wrote 'Pig' on his photograph. No doubt others, closely related to those who were deposed, might have had similar feelings. Perhaps that is why he felt he couldn't even give himself the title of Chairman.

C-H did make a move after the Second World War and before Harry was eventually appointed chairman. The chairmanship at that time was up for grabs. There were a number of good contenders. Harry, though in fact brilliant, was not universally admired. He was a late developer and had a poor academic record. Guy was very uncertain about him.

Harry's diary records a bombshell in 1947: 'C-H tried to push me and Geoff out.' Unfortunately, neither history nor anybody's memory can add much to that cryptic entry. Searching his diary around that time reveals problems with ownership of a major outlet for flat glass in North America, a Canadian company called Duplate. Duplate was owned three ways – by Pilkington, PPG (the largest American glassmaker), and Phillips, a Canadian businessman. Pilkington was offered Phillips' share and for reasons unknown failed to clinch it, so Duplate fell into PPG's control. Harry records that he was double-crossed by Phillips and PPG. Whatever the reason, Harry took responsibility for the failure.

Edward Cozens-Hardy came from a notable family from Norfolk. His father held the top legal post in the nation – Master of the Rolls. As you might expect of the son of a top lawyer, Edward had a rather good set of genes (Figure 13). It showed in the family – his sister, Hope, who married Austin, was a top-class mathematician. Hope contented herself with – devoted herself to – bringing up a family of five who all had distinguished careers: Harry and Lawrence who were in the firm, Roger, a noted writer, Margaret, head of the Girl Guides, and Constance, an Oxford don.

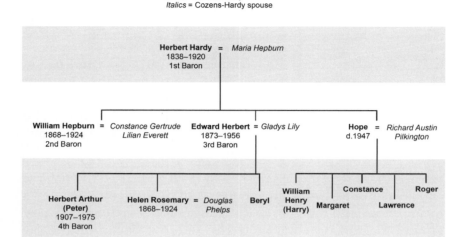

Bold = Cozens-Hardy
Italics = Cozens-Hardy spouse

Herbert Hardy = *Maria Hepburn*
1838–1920
1st Baron

William Hepburn = *Constance Gertrude*   **Edward Herbert** = *Gladys Lily*   **Hope** = *Richard Austin*
1868–1924   *Lilian Everett*   1873–1956   d.1947   *Pilkington*
2nd Baron   3rd Baron

Herbert Arthur   **Helen Rosemary** = *Douglas*   **Beryl**   **William**   **Constance**   **Roger**
(Peter)   1868–1924   *Phelps*   **Henry**   **Margaret**   **Lawrence**
1907–1975   **(Harry)**
4th Baron

Figure 13   Cozens-Hardy family tree

Elizabeth Williams-Ellis (pp. 114–15) takes the view that it was the Cozens-Hardy injection that saved the company after the nadir of the third generation. The mixing of Cozens-Hardy and Pilkington genes was bound to be a winner. The winner, the outstanding progeny, was Harry (later Sir Harry).

So what happened when C-H took charge? He reorganised the company and gave people specific jobs. His organisation was as follows:

> Geoffrey was appointed chairman a year later, in 1932 (fourth generation). He remained chairman until Harry took charge in 1949.
>
> Grove Street works (sheet and rolled plate) and timber yard – G. R. (Guy) Pilkington (assisted by Douglas Phelps).
>
> Cowley Hill and Doncaster plate glass works – R. M. Weeks.

Ravenhead works (cathedral and miscellaneous) –
Geoffrey Pilkington (assisted by R. K. Uhthoff)

Planning and propaganda – Geoffrey Pilkington.

Technical services – R. M. Weeks (assisted by Douglas
Phelps).

Sales and commercial departments – W. S. Tunnock
(assisted by Harry Pilkington and William Lee Pilkington).

Financial department, accounts, costs, cash –
E. Cozens-Hardy.

Legal department, estate, property, patents – J. H.
Dickinson.

Secretarial department – W. S. Tunnock (assisted by J. B.
Finlay, who was to become company secretary in May 1932).

It will be noted that new names appear – some old stagers, some
Young Turks. Of the old stagers my father, G. R. (Guy) Pilkington,
took this appointment as constructive dismissal and promptly
retired. Norman, who was appointed chairman for a short
interim period, was given no job in that list. His mind had gone.

Of the non-family names, most were old stagers (Tunnock and
Dickinson were directors). Finlay was company secretary for
many years. Uhthoff, a dynamic young recruit, died young.
A name that stands out is R. M. Weeks. He got a job top as
manager of both Plate Works and Doncaster. He was C-H's
right-hand man (axe man) in C-H's reorganisation, a very
capable person who eventually became General Sir Ronald
Weeks, deputy chairman of the Imperial General Staff. He would
have been implicated in my father's move.

Guy and Weeks must have been reconciled at a later date. When
Weeks was a guest of my father (Father rented a Scottish deer
forest) he was the only one who was allowed to bag a Royal

(a 12-pointer). The rest of us had to be part of father's strategy – improve the breed by culling the Switches (stags with few points).

C-H brought in new non-family blood as well as putting the family Turks through a rigorous regime. In fact, Barker records that C-H kept these family apprentices much longer in training than had previously been the practice.

The other names that stand out are Harry (Sir Harry, who became chairman of the board in 1949) and Douglas Phelps (who became chairman of the Executive in 1945). Young Harry was singled out by fate at this time. He was in training to be part of the sales side (he did not have a technical degree). Because of deaths and retirements, he found himself in 1935, at the age of 30, the most senior person on the sales side, and a director too. This was a harsh training period for him. Business was slack during the Great Depression in the decade before the First World War. Competition was severe. Harry became highly trained (and an expert) in persuading competitors not to cut each other's throats. Pilkington having now a near monopoly in the UK, this activity was on an international scale.

During this period of uncertainty, Pilkington established one area of certainty – in technology. It had at last (after a gap of 30 years) got its window glass making technology right. Pilkington, however, was a follower rather than a leader in this particular technology, having come into it late.

Window glass was now being made by the obvious method whereby the sheet was drawn flat straight from the molten state (called the PPG process). This process produced cheap, adequate-quality flat glass and would remain in place for another 30 years until superseded by float.

Plate glass was a different matter. Since having worked with the Ford Motor Company in the 1920s, Pilkington led the world in this field. It got to the pinnacle of plate glass making in the period of C-H's leadership by the development of the twin grinder. This was a wonder of engineering whereby a fragile ribbon of cast glass, sometimes as thin as $\frac{1}{8}$" and 130" wide, was ground on both sides (top and bottom) at the same time in one machine, producing a perfectly flat satin finish for feeding to the glass polishing machine (Figure 14). The twin process remained in place until superseded by float.

During the C-H period, Pilkington attempted a number of marketing initiatives which were not successful. The names of two began with the letter 'V' – Vitaglass and Vitrolite. Vitaglass was a 'white glass' (very low in iron) which allowed healthy ultraviolet light through. One can imagine that Austin's brush with TB might have been a motivation for this initiative. It failed. Ultraviolet light coming into a room fades the carpets and curtains and takes the polish off furniture. Under Vitaglass the bugs grew faster than the plants.

Vitrolite lasted longer. It was coloured opaque glass used in place of tiles. (The first Mersey Tunnel was lined throughout with Vitrolite.) This product was unsuccessful and was discontinued in 1960. It could not compete in the end with cheap ceramic tiles and the infinite colour range of plastic tiles. Attempts to make Vitrolite by the float process helped a lot in building up the know-how necessary for the real thing.

Other initiatives were glass tubing for fluorescent lights, high-voltage insulators for the national grid, and cathode ray tubes for TVs. None of these initiatives developed into a viable long-term business. The two major additions to the company portfolio, Optical and Fibreglass, were to arrive after the Second World War under Sir Harry's charge.

C-H's right-hand man, Weeks, had shown interest in linking up with Corning, the powerful American glassmaker. This initiative was cut short by the Second World War but resurfaced to no avail in the 1970s, and in my hindsight opinion should have been pursued with much greater vigour.

PLATE GLASS – TWIN GRINDING

1. The twin grinding method was an improvement to the continuous method of plate glass production.

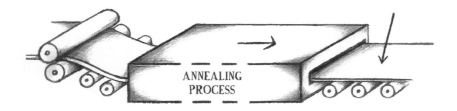

2. After annealing, the ribbon of glass enters into a grinder which smooths both sides continuously.

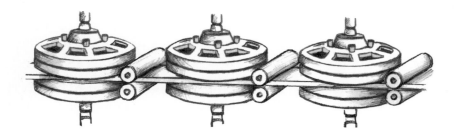

3. A method of twin polishing was never perfected, so the old method of polishing one side at a time continued to be used.

Figure 14   Plate glass – twin grinding

Another failed initiative during this period was a big step for this relatively small glass company into the capturing of a wider market – the manufacture in the 1920s of glass in the Empire. A cylinder drawn plant had been put down in Canada at a place called Thorold, 40 miles east of Toronto, in 1922. It was the obvious step for Pilkington to take when embarking on overseas expansion to start somewhere in the British Empire. They already had depots and agents around the world pushing glass made in St Helens. The moves overseas had to be approached with care. Local overseas markets might not be big enough, and if they were, exports from St Helens would be diminished.

Thorold was a failure. It closed in 1922, but it provided a foothold for one of the unsung heroes who contributed to the fourth generation's story, James Bonar Watt, whose powerful steadying influence in all production matters was invaluable for the whole span of the fourth generation. 'JBW', as he was called, was a supporter of float glass when others wobbled. He had joined the company in 1914 and was soon posted to Thorold to cut his teeth on glassmaking. Thorold failed through no fault of his, and he returned to St Helens to take charge of the newcomer – the PPG flat drawn process.

Thorold was a false start to what later, after the Second World War, became very successful overseas manufacturing initiatives in South Africa and Australia (and, for the second time, Canada). These will be covered in Chapter 10.

The Second World War had a similar effect on Pilkington's top management as had the First. Key people were called away to serve the country – Weeks, Phelps and Arthur Pilkington. Weeks, now Lord Weeks, came back after the war in a non-executive capacity and was a key figure on the top board of directors called the General Board. Harry was chairman by then, but it was as if we were reporting to Weeks, he was such a powerful presence. We were giving him an account of our stewardship. My father, Guy, and ex-chairman Geoffrey also sat on this board, but hardly said anything when they did attend.

Douglas Phelps came back from the war to chair the executive board, in effect vice-chairman to Geoffrey Pilkington, who had been chairman all through C-H's manoeuvres, and the Great Depression and the Second World War. Geoffrey handed over to Harry in 1949.

Geoffrey was a product of the rather unfocused management at the end of the third generation. Although a member of the fourth generation he was by far the eldest, nineteen years older than the eldest of the Young Turks. He was charming, debonair (bow tie), laid back, humorous. On a visit to the works in later life, asked what he thought, he replied, 'Same as ever. Smells of producer gas and stale piss!' He was not a Master of Industry but he held Pilkington together over a very difficult period.

Arthur came back to occupy a senior position, including deputy chairman under Harry, with Lawrence the technical director.

The Young Turks of the fourth generation were now in positions of power. The Pilkington family was back in control. They had the tide running with them and they were handling it well. The advent of float was still nearly a decade away.

Chapter Eight

Mother (Fantasy Number 3)

How my mother, Margery, came to St Helens.

(*Fantasy in italics. Reality in roman.*)

The four Frost sisters were a happy family, who got on well with each other and their parents. Father, Walter, was very much a man of the world, cigar smoking, successful, a prosperous art dealer. Their mother, Amy, a loving, commonsense woman.

They had all been anxious about Walter, who seemed to take the unfolding events in the world very personally. The sinking of the Titanic was, he felt, like a clarion call to the proud Victorian scientists and engineers, 'You are not the Masters of the Universe'.

And then there was the menacing advance of the German military across Europe and their mighty fleet of capital ships, equally menacing. This was not a gentlemanly affair, this was war to the death.

'Do you remember saying how boring life used to be, Eleanor?', her mother remarked one morning at breakfast.

'Well, it was.'

'Eleanor's right', Edith chimed in. 'The only excitement we've had was Father moving us out of Bristol to here.'

Walter's plans for his daughters followed the typical mode of that era – find them a husband, hopefully wealthy, from a higher class, namely the County Set. He had already moved his principal dwelling twenty miles north from Bristol to Almondsbury in the hope of a suitable catch, since, in his opinion, the Bristol men were unsuitable. A man of considerable energy (one of the maids had had to take a holiday in order to nurse a by-product of his energy), Walter had built a fine redbrick mansion suitable to his status as a business leader poised for the next rung of the social ladder. He also, ahead of his time, had insured against marriage failure by seeing that his daughters were trained for professions.

'And it's still boring! We've had not a single decent invitation to any balls or dinners. Our own efforts to host a soirée earlier this year fell flat with so many refusals.'

'Snobs, that's what they are.'

'At least in Bristol there was some social life.'

'Now, my dears, don't take on so. You know your father is right. Something is bound to turn up soon.'

'Will it? Come on, Mother, you know very well that all the good men are going off to the war.'

'And getting killed!'

The last speaker was Margery (my mother, yet to be so!). Little did she know that something was to turn up within twelve hours of her remark.

An official-looking letter lay on the breakfast table the very next day addressed to Margery Frost. The excitement of the family was palpable. The letter was from the War Office.

Margery, after a rigorous training under a Swedish martinet called Madam Osterberg, was anxious to get to work as a masseuse. The war was at its most intense on the Western Front. News of the carnage on the battlefields was filtering through, but the country remained solidly behind Lloyd George and continued to volunteer.

Women were as keen as men to play their part, and the letter from the War Office no doubt fulfilled Margery's desires in that direction. She was born number three into a family of four girls; her father, Walter Frost, most of all wanted a son to follow him into his business as an art dealer, but although thwarted in this desire, he was still keen that his daughters should do well. It was reported that Walter had gone into his local tobacconist soon after Margery was born, to be greeted by 'Another disappointment, Mr Frost!' His second daughter, Edith, fitted the bill and became a very successful chair of his art business, Frost & Reed.

Now, on reading the letter from the War Office, Walter expressed his disdain. 'To Miss Margery Frost. You are hereby directed to relocate to St Helens, Lancashire, to take up the appointment of masseur in the Pilkington Orthopaedic Hospital as soon as possible.' The letter also gave contact names and addresses.

'Lancashire! Of all places! Smoke, chimneys, fog, grit, poverty. An industrial hellhole. With prospects like that, she should stay here at home.'

Amy calmed him down. 'Walter, you are pre-judging the place. I'm sure that there will be suitable people for Margery to meet there. She's twenty-eight. She's ready for a challenge. Your much-vaunted move to Almondsbury has not yielded any prospects of any value. I hear that the Derbys of Knowsley Hall, Lancashire, are good people!'

So Margery duly arrived in St Helens.

She received a typically warm North Country welcome from her landlady. Her digs were comfortable and spotless.

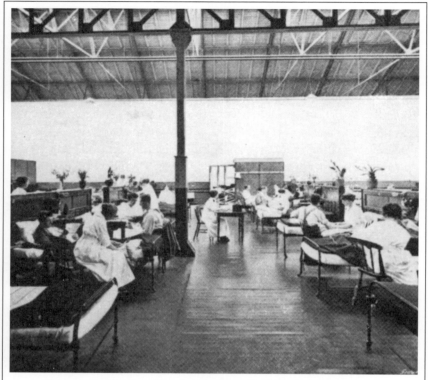

Plate 7   Pilkington Special Orthopedic Hospital, Ravenhead

The introduction to the Orthopedic Hospital (Plate 7) was no less welcoming. Margery was soon to meet the head of the hospital, Dr Kerr, who told her of the background to the creation of the hospital.

He had been the Pilkington company doctor and he was also practising surgeon since the dangers of the glass industry and severe injuries required that the company doctor should be a surgeon. During the war he had met a famous French orthopaedic surgeon and his experiences with him and the war-wounded in France had given him a desire to set up something similar in England.

At about the same time, he had been in on a discussion with the Pilkington partners about a problem they had with making armaments for the war effort. The Pilkingtons had no problem in supporting the war effort and making the shell cases; the issue for them was what to do with the substantial profits from armaments. So Dr Kerr suggested that the Pilkingtons build an orthopaedic hospital, which, with his new-found knowledge, he would supervise.

He emerged from the discussion with solid backing for his idea. However, the Pilkingtons insisted that the hospital should be open for 'other ranks'. The officer classes were better provided for in the big mansions of the County Set.

Dr Kerr's view was that the hospital should concentrate on post-operative rehabilitation and should be not only for the war-wounded, but also for those seriously damaged in the manufacture of flat glass.

Margery had been as impressed by Dr Kerr as the Pilkingtons had been. He was an exciting person to work with, and his ideas were unimpeachable.

One day when Margery was on duty in a ward, a lady accompanied Dr Kerr as if she were on an official visit. The party approached where Margery was working.

'Margery, I'd like you to meet Mrs Arthur Pilkington.'

'How nice to meet you, Margery.' Mrs Arthur – the Pilkington wives were called like this – smiled a welcoming, friendly smile. 'How nice, my name is Marjorie too.'

The two Margerys (Marjories) chatted happily for a while before the party moved away round the ward. 'I hope to see you again.'

'Who was that?' enquired Margery. 'Oh, don't you know? She's the wife of the chairman of the glassworks.'

'What a charming lady.'

And so it was that an envelope duly arrived for Margery, inviting her to Windle Hall for tea with Mrs Arthur Pilkington.

A carriage called for her a day later. Margery stepped into it. Father would be impressed by this, thought Margery. This was not any old vehicle but one of the latest designs. Her eyes took it all in. The groom was immaculate, the horse prize-winning, and the interior sumptuous.

Windle Hall was approached by a long drive and was set in its own extensive grounds on top of a hill on the edge of St Helens. These Pilkingtons were not ordinary tradesmen. Margery felt warm inside.

She had heard from Dr Kerr that the Pilkington glassworks was the first in the Kingdom and nearly a hundred years old.

Arthur had been spared from the Western Front as chairman of an essential industry. But others of the family had not. Guy was wounded twice. Norman went through the whole war wounded mentally rather than physically.

It was at a party at Windle Hall that Margery was to meet the war hero, Guy, recovering from his wounds. Margery was immediately attracted to this handsome soldier, but it was only later that she made up her mind.

Guy, 35, must have felt huge relief at surviving the war. He had done his duty. He had survived the awful miasma of the Western Front ('the world's worst wound': Sassoon), and now his thoughts could turn to romance.

Into his ken swims this good-looking, well-spoken Margery Frost. She was ideal – age 28 and from a respectable and suitable family (the same class – 'trade').

My mother told me that she made up her mind to marry him at a military parade in Queens Park, St Helens. There was a young lad (an 'urchin' he would have been called in those days) who was causing a nuisance by getting among the troops. She saw Capt. Guy Pilkington deal with the matter firmly and humanely. 'I'm going to marry that man!'

The wartime romance blossomed quickly. Within six months of their first meeting at Windle Hall they were married. Their first child, Godfrey, was born seven days before the Armistice.

Guy and Margery settled down in a large house two miles north-west of St Helens called Fairfield. They finished with five children, of which David was the fourth. After their parents died the children, with help from the Pilkington family, the Pilkington company and many others, turned Fairfield into a 60-bed independent hospital. Most of those who worked there had known Guy and Margery personally. The Pilkington Orthopedic Hospital closed in 1925. Fairfield is still (2010) working.

A hospital to start and a hospital to finish!

Chapter Nine

Father (1881–1970)

My father, Guy, had a somewhat chequered experience in early life. He was the youngest of eight and his mother had become tired of bearing children. Pregnant yet again, she was appalled. It is easy to see why the thought rather upset her. But duty called. Duty to her husband, and duty to the Pilkington dynasty to produce as many boys as possible.

Guy was born in an old Elizabethan manor called Lion House, which his father, Rainford Richard, had purchased near (two miles) to the glassworks, with a plot of land to match. Lion House was now too small and Richard decided to enlarge it on the same site. The site was so good – so near St Helens, and near a railway station for travel afield.

The wholesale shift must have been unsettling for Guy. The family now found themselves residing in the Prince of Wales Hotel in Southport. More suitable temporary accommodation was arranged by taking over a house called Muncaster Hall, at Rainford, some two miles further away.

The cost of the enlarged Lion House and the time taken to build it are unknown to me, except the cost overran and so, no doubt, did the time. This overrun apparently so upset Richard that he insisted the contractor should only be paid the original estimated sum. Richard was sitting pretty financially. He caused the contractor to go bankrupt.

Back in the extended house, now called Rainford Hall, Guy no doubt was happy with his own quarters, with a nanny to love him and much fun exploring the new house and relaid grounds, including a new pond with a boat. His teenage years were spent at a public school (Clifton College, Bristol), and then Cambridge for a degree in History. He would be enjoying the halcyon days which occurred under Edward VII. The British Empire ruled the world. Peace was established. Everybody knew their place.

At the age of twenty-seven Guy was hit by a devastating blow. My grandfather died, and at the reading of the will Guy learned that he had been left his out. He had been chosen to be what he had always suspected, an orphan unloved by his mother, abandoned by his father.

As in all pain, of course, there were those who made up for the loss. Guy was greatly loved by his two elder sisters, Edith and Evelyn. His elder brother, Norman, began wondering how to care for him, and later set up a trust to balance the discrepancy in wealth.

The other major event that was to affect his life was the outbreak of the Great War. Guy was now 33. He had lived in the shadow of his elder brother, who was more confident, better-looking and a better dancer. Norman got the girls.

Father found that he could dance, but it required great concentration on his part. He told me that his first words when approaching a girl were 'We can talk or we can dance'.

Guy would have welcomed the war. At that time there was a great upswelling of patriotism. Those who avoided joining up received white feathers ('coward!').

Guy would have entered a new family who would meet all his needs – the 5th South Lancs Territorial Army Regiment. The men were all local and many were ex-Pilkington employees. Guy, as a Pilkington carrying demi-royal status, would quickly become an officer. Norman became Colonel of the Regiment and Guy finally succeeded to that title when Norman died nearly twenty years later.

The second crushing blow came to Guy as the 'noble' battle against Germany turned into the 'world's worst wound', in the mud of the killing fields of the Somme and Flanders. Guy was wounded, and came home to recuperate at Rainford Hall as a hero. He suffered a third serious wound and was finally invalided out to take up an Army training position.

General acceptance of post-traumatic stress syndrome was completely lacking after the First World War. Father was rescued from it by a young lady, Margery Frost, my mother. How that came about has been related in Chapter 8, 'Mother'.

Norman was not rescued. He lost his mind. He never received any treatment. The head works chauffeur was 'very good with him' when he became awkward, for example putting on his evening dress and going out in the middle of the night. He lived at home. He never married, and died young at 65.

As part of the third generation (who 'nearly lost it'), Guy was not a businessman and would have been subservient to the two forceful members of that generation, his first cousins, Austin and Cecil. Guy went on to have a successful career in the glassworks. Though not a businessman he played a leading role in establishing Pilkington as a caring company.

Guy, in his family role, was a passionate conservationist. He annually visited Scotland where he actively encouraged those who were in his party to shoot only the poor-looking stags. This was combined with an anachronism – only standard sights were to be used on rifles, not telescopic sights. He was also fanatical about the saving of domestic water. We were discouraged from flushing the loo. Hot baths were to be minimal as to frequency and water level.

In her 1997 book *The Pilkington Story*, Elizabeth Williams-Ellis relates the following:

Another example of devotion to duty is that evinced by Guy
Reginald (1881–1970) ... after what became known as 'The Big Row'
in 1931 when he, together with his cousins Austin the Chairman and
Cecil, was forced to resign from the Board, a time when feeling ran
so high that Guy's wife Margery, who greatly resented the way he
had been treated, wrote the word 'pig' across the photograph
of Edward Cozens-Hardy, who, assisted by Ronald Weeks, was
regarded as the architect of the putsch.

Shortly afterwards, the works were faced with the possibility of a
strike over an attempt to introduce an American piece work system
known as 'The Bedaux System'. The men very much resented aspects
of this proposal, notably that some of their performance related
rewards were to be paid to the foremen.

Guy was much liked by the workforce, who respected his fair-
mindedness and felt he would understand their point of view. The
Board from which he had been ejected asked him to come into the
works to try to settle the dispute. His wife endeavoured to prevent
him doing so. Guy simply said, 'It is my duty to the family', went
back to the works and settled the strike. (p. 92)

Another nice story is told about Guy. He was churchwarden at
his local Anglican church, where he read the lesson every Sunday.
One Sunday, after he had completed the first lesson, he sat down
next to my mother, who whispered:

'Couldn't hear a word of that.'

'You weren't supposed to!'

What was the reading from the Bible that was so naughty it
wasn't fit to be read in church? It was the story of King David,
who was now so old that he couldn't keep warm, so they gave
him a young virgin, to

lie in thy bosom, that my lord the king may get heat. (1 Kings 1: 2)

This they did. It worked! But the king 'knew her not'.

Part Two

Windows of Change:
From Float to the Present

Chapter Ten

The Fourth Generation (1945–1970)

After the Second World War, the Glass Act enters an entirely new phase. We move into somewhat uncharted waters. The author is a participant as well as an observer.

Up to this point, the history is fairly well-established. Theo Barker has written the business side thoroughly. Elizabeth Williams-Ellis has made important new connections to the family. Tom Grundy has told what it was like to be a glassworker. David Bricknell covers the later period 1950–85.

Up to this point the story has been about the older generations, my predecessors. The business was undoubtedly and pointedly a family business. After 1945 Pilkington was big on the national stage, but limited on the world stage: a monopoly in the United Kingdom but the smallest of half a dozen names in the world of equivalent size.

Things were about to change in a big way. This was through the advent of float, which was to catapult Pilkington to world prominence.

This part of the Glass Act is much more challenging to write about. I was deeply immersed among the trees, how could I possibly see the wood? It is almost impossible to be impartial because I knew only a part. As a director you are supposed to comprehend the whole, but I found that impossible to do. Indeed

I confess that I wasn't greatly interested in the rest, only my bit.

So I return to my original stance. I am writing this book for fun. It is for my grandchildren. It does not claim to be authoritative or scholarly or complete.

It was on Sir Harry's watch that two great events of the Glass Act took place:

1.   The climax of the Glass Act, the invention of the float process (1952).

2.   The end of the Glass Act, the flotation(!) of the company on the Stock Market (1970).

There was a third event of major importance at that period which, although life-changing at the time, could not rank in significance with the first two, and this was the revolt of the workers, the seven-week strike of all the St Helens glassworkers (1970).

I move away from the chronology of the early chapters of this book to look at each of these events in detail in separate chapters. As well as looking at each in detail, it is interesting to look for connecting factors between them.

There were two areas of the company's life which were 'hurting'. One was finance, the other was people, the two key aspects of any business.

On the financial front, float was demanding serious access to capital beyond the means of a private company. This could be remedied by opening up ownership to many more shareholders and unlimited capital – the flotation of the company on the Stock Market – but it was not the only option.

On the human front, all the production workers went on strike and closed the company down for seven weeks. We could not apply a remedy because we did not know the cause of the strike

– and neither did the majority of the strikers! These factors seriously impinged on the life of the company in their different ways. It was a time of uncertainty. How these problems were solved will be covered in this and subsequent chapters.

In the meantime, there was a cohesive force within the company that held everything together. That force was the 'lucky' personality of Sir Harry Pilkington. His chairmanship was so effective that it coincided with the golden age of the Glass Act. (There had been an earlier golden age a century before.)

Although Sir Harry dominated this age (did he create it, or did it just happen?), he had a powerful and capable team under him. A non-family director remarked to me how becoming a director felt like joining a brotherhood.

I am not going to pick out any names of Harry's team, nor of all those others who supported them, unless the text demands it. There is one name, however, that forces attention and that is the inventor of float – Alastair (his name was actually Lionel Alexander Bethune).

The Pilkingtons' devotion to their mission over four generations was finally and truly rewarded by the discovery of the Holy Grail of the flat glass business. Along comes this distant cousin, Alastair (so distant that the genealogical connection has never been made, despite much effort), who is taken on as a family trainee (with all the privileges that went with that). This distant cousin then pays back the faith of those who took him on, a thousandfold.

Alastair told me that the person who persuaded him to join was Douglas Phelps, the deputy chairman. Harry was 'prickly'. I think Harry was concerned at the entry route that had been taken. The time-honoured method was that any partner (as they called themselves) could nominate one family member as a family trainee. Alastair had not been nominated by a partner. I think, also, that Harry, a staunch Congregationalist (who was not happy when his son, John, became an Anglican priest), was really suspicious of Alastair's religion, Christian Science – what on earth was *that*!

Alastair had completed his engineering degree, started before the war and disrupted by four years as a German prisoner. Arguably, his time in prison formed his gifts as much as Cambridge University. The Germans treated their captives well, provided that they were officers. Alastair was confined to one room shared with around two hundred others. He had to learn to concentrate or there was a risk of going mad. It gave him a lifelong skill in music, the ability to play the clarinet, but, most of all, the capacity for intense concentration. (Once, at a meeting on the ground floor, a fire engine drove up towards the window, which Alastair was facing, siren sounding, and turned left into the works. After the meeting someone said, 'I wonder where the fire engine went?' Alastair: 'What fire engine?')

There will be more on Alastair later. First we must focus on the leader of the fourth generation – Sir Harry Pilkington. Harry's name was actually William Henry. He was a late developer. He was not encouraged by his father (Austin). His mother? We know she was somewhat puritanical. A newly married daughter-in-law is having breakfast in the Austin–Hope household. With toast on her plate, she reaches for the butter and then for the marmalade. 'Either butter *or* marmalade, dear – not both!'

Harry attended Magdalene College, Cambridge, where he got an inauspicious third-class degree in history and economics. He was not an academic (he probably did not see the point). However, he had a powerful mind and an amazing memory assisted by the regular keeping of a five-year diary. He had a head for financial figures. He had broad vision.

He had had instilled into him a lifelong loyalty to the Congregational Church, and rarely failed to attend Chapel on a Sunday morning. He believed in the gospel of hard work and strict self-discipline. He had the business ability to see two steps ahead of everybody else. When he played tennis (or Scrabble) he always had to win. He could do the *Times* crossword puzzle in ten minutes. All these attributes were to stand him in good stead throughout his life.

When Geoffrey retired as chairman in 1949 Harry wasn't the obvious choice. My father, Guy, was not a supporter. C-H (Edward Cozens-Hardy) had tried to push him off the board. Harry had made a major mistake (see later in this chapter), but nevertheless the appointment was made.

Luck smiled on him. Within three years of Harry becoming chairman, Alastair invented float. Harry, though not a technical man, could see immediately that this was the ultimate way to make clear flat glass. He saw two steps ahead – if this were to work it could be exploited worldwide and give Pilkington the opportunity to carve up the world flat glass business. The two steps ahead were needed (three in fact) – it took six years from the invention in 1952 to the first piece of saleable glass, another two years to profitability, and another four years before the total development costs had been paid back.

Total development costs were around £7 million. Would a modern money-man have agreed to such an investment over such a long time span? Although float was profitable by the end of 1960, it did not repay the development costs until 1964.

So when Luck smiled on Harry he seized the moment with both hands. He knew what *he* had to do: give Alastair continuing and unflagging support, which meant keeping the finance flowing through thin (glass) and thick, including riding over some board members' understandable doubts.

Harry was a giant. By force of personality (plus his personal gifts, plus float) he held the supply and demand for flat glass in balance worldwide. This kept prices and profitability up. He was very strong in his belief that cut-throat competition did nobody any good. He wanted strong competition, by which he meant that Pilkington should have competitors and the competitors should be strong. This was best for the long-term health of the industry. He travelled the world meeting the large customers. He also met the heads of the competitors face to face, in some cases making them personal friends. Harry's methods would have run foul of modern anti-trust legislation.

In the mid 1960s, Pilkington was approached by the UK Monopolies Commission, which had come to investigate the supply of flat glass (including safety glass) in the UK. The Commission produced a uniquely positive report which welcomed the company policies and which praised its responsible position as a monopoly and its concern for the public interest (Barker 1977, p. 411).

What was it like to work with Sir Harry? He was the overshadowing, dominant presence. He dominated any meeting he attended. He always knew what to do. He was totally trusted. He was a man without guile. He had no hidden agendas. He carried his load easily. We seldom had to go to him with problems. We knew our place in the organisation and we knew what to do.

Harry was interested and alert regarding all aspects of the business, including my world of human relations, pensions and welfare, particularly pensions and welfare. He was a member of the Joint Industrial Council (the main negotiating body), the main pension fund trustee organisation, and the board that ran the Welfare Organisation.

Float – development, exploitation, licensing, major worldwide investment, defending the patent – soon came to dominate the board's thinking. Luck continued to smile on Harry, as the post-war demand for glass resulted in record profits and, therefore, the resources required to finance the float development.

The demand for flat glass was insatiable. The bomb damage in many major UK cities (including, of course, London) as well as in cities in Europe, plus damage to the European glassmaking works, gave Pilkington the ideal position of a suppliers' market – the glass merchants had to accept that they were rationed. It was also, of course, a profitable time. The 1950s were a time of extraordinary optimism for the company. This profitable time allowed Pilkington to finance float, but also to look at a wider market than the UK. They already had agents worldwide, but also depots in which St Helens glass was stored for immediate supply to customers.

The first expansion plan was to establish glassmaking facilities in the British Empire. Canada was the first, then South Africa, also Argentina, and a share of an Australian glassworks was purchased. (There had been two failed initiatives involving overseas production at about the time of the First World War: plate glass at Maubeuge in France, and sheet at Thorold in Canada.)

The suppliers' market continued for about ten years after the Second World War, by which time the seductive promise of a bright future – float – was dawning. Efforts to keep good relationships with competitors continued. There was more serendipity – the American glass plants of LOF and PPG were on strike, and the profit on the glass sold to them virtually funded the float project. The lure of the huge potential market in North America always loomed large in the company's consciousness, particularly when the Canadian sheet plant was established in 1947.

This was the setting for Harry's 'mistake', which took place before he became chairman. What exactly was this, that it should haunt him for the remainder of his life? Was it really a mistake?

One of the reasons for establishing a glassworks early in any territory is the obvious one, to deter competitors from doing the same. A local glassworks could, by its very presence, capture a large share of the local demand and on its back encourage local customers to buy other products from St Helens.

In Canada there was already an important customer, Duplate. Duplate took raw flat glass and processed it into safety glass to supply the motor car manufacturers both in Canada and North America. A vital outlet for the makers of the raw glass to control.

Duplate was, as mentioned above, owned one third each by two companies and one individual – Pilkington, PPG, and a Canadian citizen, W. E. Phillips. The understanding was that if Phillips wanted to sell his one-third ownership, Pilkington had first refusal.

Harry, not yet chairman, was the director responsible for Canada. He took on the negotiations about Duplate. There was only one answer, 'Yes'. Then the haggling began. Phillips, knowing the importance of Duplate to both companies, drove too hard a bargain for Harry. The negotiations were called off. Instead of Phillips coming back to Harry, he settled with PPG, behind Harry's back. On 21 March 1947 Harry wrote in his diary, 'Phillips and PPG double-crossed us. Shameful day.'

The message about this fateful loss of control of a major glass outlet reached St Helens by transatlantic telephone, to be taken by the deputy chairman, Douglas Phelps (the worldwide telephone network was still in its infancy at that time):

'He's a skunk, Colonel.'

'What's that, Harrison? I can't quite catch that.'

'He's a skunk, Colonel, a dirty skunk.'

Harrison, the Pilkington manager in Canada, knew the significance of what had happened very well. Harrison no doubt kicked himself that he hadn't been more diligent behind the scenes.

So, there it is, Harry's major business 'mistake'. You can see why it should have haunted him. North America is the hardest place in the world in which to do business, without having to carry an albatross round your neck. Nevertheless, the Canadian setback did not stop Pilkington buying into the number two American glassmaker, LOF, which was to lead to an early association with Nippon Sheet Glass, the present (2008–) owner of Pilkington.

Arguably, another American opportunity was missed. This was to link up with Corning Glass, the most progressive of the American glassmakers and specifically not in flat glass, thus avoiding anti-trust legislation in both countries. Such a link might have carried the company through the post-float era, where, to some extent, the plot was lost. (See Chapter 14, 'The Fifth Generation'.)

Having climbed Mount Everest, what do you do next? What is there after such a climax? Life was no longer simple. Flat glass didn't offer the old challenge any more. Everybody could now make perfect glass. Flat glass was now just a commodity, no more interesting than a common brick.

The answer is clever glass. Glass of all kinds – to keep out the heat of the sun in summer and keep in the warmth in winter. Glass able to clean itself. Coloured glass. Decorative glass. Glass strong enough to support itself in the form of a complete façade uninterrupted by frames (Plate 8). The remarkable thing is that a number of these offshoot products can be manufactured in the float bath using the properties of electrical conductivity manifest in glass at about 800°C.

This account of the fourth generation, the golden age of the Glass Act, is somewhat partial, as it has concentrated chiefly on the arrival of float and the company's Stock Market flotation. A huge range of other activities were also going on, which required the highest skill and the greatest dedication from the board and management. Optical was built into a major world business. The company was involved in fibre optics for communications, in glass-fibre-reinforced cement, in solar cells.

Fibreglass was built from nothing into a major arm. Before the Second World War it had been treated as a 'toy' and of no significance. In order to kick-start Pilk's late entry into what was already a major world business, a top-level executive was hired from outside. He became a director within three years. (This had never happened so fast before – up to this point non-family directors had always been appointed from within and only after long service.) His name was Alan Hudson-Davies.

Alan turned out to have 'unusual' dimensions. He had already pre-warned the board that he was a dedicated socialist. (My father, Guy, used to mutter 'Hudson-Davies, Hudson-Davies, good man, but he votes Labour, you know'.) Another dimension was his moral courage. At a board meeting, he suddenly said:

> Excuse me, chairman, but that decision was not taken by this board, was it? There is an apartheid on this board. Some of us are 'Peter', 'Douglas', 'Lawrence'. The rest are 'Hudson-Davies', 'Watt', 'McOnie' …

The reply was dead silence (that's what it felt like), but quickly the point was taken and we all became 'C-H', 'DVP', 'LHAP', 'AH-D', 'JBW', 'GMcO' … An important brick in the apartheid wall had been removed, though not the final brick.

And what was Alastair like? Although taken on as a family member, he had to start at the bottom as a technical assistant. He had to learn the ropes. He had no privileges. He was not on any decision-making body. The surprising thing was, it seemed as if he didn't need to be taught how to make glass. Although he was supposed to be learning, he was immediately contributing. One of his many talents was the ability to apply advanced mathematics to glassmaking, and his outstanding talent was his ability to focus on what really mattered.

Alastair was a humble man. Very approachable. Very wise. I often came home saying to my wife, 'Alastair says …' One of his fundamental beliefs was that fear was a 'very bad decision-maker'. Another saying of his was that we needed to 'express wisdom in the Eternal Now' – I think that they were phrases

Plate 8   Atrium, Judiciary Square, Washington DC

coined by the Christian Scientists. He was also quite clear that humanity and efficiency were not at odds with each other, but complementary. He had a cottage in the Lake District where he used to escape to to walk and to think. He was a good advertisement for Christian Science.

Alastair was a complex person. He was good at sports (a triple half-blue at Cambridge; squash, fives and tennis), and a competent yachtsman. He was at his best in technical discussions and gave good leadership. His four years as a prisoner of war had a big effect on him, as did a dominant Christian Scientist mother. He was a loyal supporter of anyone who put the company's interests first.

There is an interesting and extraordinary aspect to his life – he had three 'close shaves' when death threatened to take him. The first incident occurred when he was walking with his family in the Lake District, when a big storm blew up and he was struck by lightning. He carried on walking, and the only result was a headache the next morning.

The second incident was when he was on holiday in Canada with a friend from St Helens (Dr John Manning?). He met up with Dr Lawrence Pilkington and his wife, Norah, and they undertook a canoeing expedition on a lake. Alastair insisted on paddling his own canoe (accompanied by John). Lawrence and Norah, knowing how quickly and viciously a storm could blow up, pressed for them each to share a canoe. Alastair dug in his heels (paddle?) and, as expected, soon turned turtle. You cannot right a Canadian canoe and you cannot get into one in the middle of a lake. You cannot stay alive in their freezing water for more than thirty minutes or so. Wisely, Lawrence and Norah had stayed close by and were able, eventually, to hail a boat. It was October and all holiday traffic had emigrated south. Lucky.

The third incident was an attempt on Alastair's life by an Irishman. His potential murderer was convicted and imprisoned. After release, he asked to meet Alastair to apologise. The advice, which Alastair took this time(!), was 'Don't do it'.

The Irishman had sent a letter bomb to Alastair's house. Alastair was on holiday (lucky!), and his post was taken by chauffeur to the office. His secretary (Mrs Wailing) looked at it suspiciously and called the company security officer. He looked at it, whereupon it blew up in his hands. Luck again intervened. It was only the detonator – the bomb ingredients themselves were scattered harmlessly all over the secretary's office.

Alastair could see early on in his career that what really mattered was a better way of forming the ribbon. The existing two ways, plate and sheet, were far from perfect. Why two ways of making flat glass? Surely there must be one universal method by which all flat glass could be made. That was the goal to aim for. The board had stated this need in 1950: 'The ultimate objective is to arrive at standards of flatness resembling those of plate without Grinding and Polishing.'

Alastair didn't get into float immediately. He had joined the company in 1947 as a family trainee. It was to be five years before he invented float, but he wasn't idle in the intervening years. Although he started in a junior position as a Technical Assistant, he was immediately contributing and working on his own ideas rather than being told what to do. The glassmaking managers were amazed at his ability to use mathematics in a real live situation. In his use of integral calculus he was a master.

Although still not a director himself, Alastair was becoming recognised as a person of outstanding intellect and ability by the directors, and it was at this point that he was given his first real promotion, to production manager of a big glassworks. He was moved from St Helens to Doncaster, where he did some preliminary work on the melting process, of which, as production manager, he was now in charge

Doncaster, being 83 miles distant from St Helens, was always recognised as being relatively free from the direct influence of the directors, who were based in St Helens. The saying was, 'There are eighty-three good reasons for working at Doncaster, every one of them a mile long.' Alastair enjoyed his freedom there. Although holding down a seriously responsible job he was able to experiment.

And finally, who was this member of the fourth generation, the author, called David?

David, born with a silver spoon in his mouth and the work's hooters in his ears, grew up in a wealthy family with privileges and some 'royal' status in St Helens. He was put through the rigorous induction programme for family trainees. An engineering graduate from Cambridge, he started, aged 22, as a technical assistant in the Technical Development department.

He was given many different experiences and tasks in his training. A significant and exciting time was spent as works manager of the small South Wales sheet glass plant at Pontypool. As well as managing the works he was looking for a wife. Evidently he was successful in both, becoming a director in 1956 and married man in 1957.

David's deal was a good one. 'You either make it to the board or you're out. No half way.'

Dr David Bricknell, in his excellent account *Float: Pilkingtons' glass revolution*, writes about David as follows:

> He was not a capitalist, red in tooth and claw, but a member of the family with a long history of slightly paternalistic but nevertheless labour friendly policies. His emphasis was on the company's long-term industrial culture of looking after the workforce, not the recent industrial culture of constant warfare. (p. 150)

David's epitaph might read: 'He was one of the manifestations of the human face of Pilkington.' Antony, the last Pilkington chairman, christened him 'Group Chief Communist'.

See Plate 9 for an illustration of the prominent members of the
fourth generation.

Plate 9   Young Turks and old stagers

Chapter Eleven

Float: The Holy Grail

If anyone has turned straight to this chapter, read on, but to some extent you will have missed the point. The float process only came about because of the constant striving for technological perfection by every generation of the Pilkingtons, but also by others, notably Henry Ford, the car manufacturer (see Chapter 5). Such steady building of the foundations was essential to the final success, and the story is meaningless without it.

Glassmakers had dreamed down the ages of making the perfect piece of flat glass, ever since glass became more commonly available in a flat form, which could be used as a window, not just to let in light but to provide an outside view as well, and, of course, as a mirror. The earliest form of flat glass was in ecclesiastical buildings, where providing a view was not necessary (indeed a view was unwelcome). These windows let in light, but instead of a view, their purpose was to let in a message for the worshippers. Some of the earliest of these stained glass windows date from the seventh century.

It was easy to imagine what the criteria for a perfect piece of flat glass would be. It would have three characteristics – perfect planimetry (no distortion), a bright (fire-finished) surface, and cheapness.

Apparent perfection was achieved by the plate process of grinding and polishing a glass blank. The result was indeed near-perfection, but very expensive compared to crown glass. In spite of missing out badly on that one crucial characteristic (price), the plate process, with its freedom from distortion, found a ready market in the high-quality end of the market. So the plate process had a long life, from its invention by the French in the seventeenth century until it was superseded by float 300 years later.

True perfection in float was not achieved until after the Second World War. Why did it take so long? The reason lies in the nature of glass when it is in a suitable state to be formed into an object. Molten glass is formed into a finished solid object at about 600°C (red hot). Above this temperature it is syrupy; below, it is gradually hardening but is floppy. This floppiness has to be controlled until the glass is solid enough to handle without marking.

Throughout this interim stage, between liquid and solid, the floppy object being formed must not touch anything which could mar the fire-finished surface or add faults to its body. There are only three methods of ensuring this:

Method 1.   A gob of molten glass on the end of a rotating iron rod or blowpipe is kept rotating until set (the crown process).

Method 2.   A ribbon of glass is lifted vertically up a tower, where no roller or conveyor touches its surface until it is set (the flat drawn process).

Method 3.   Molten glass is poured onto molten tin and moved over the molten tin, cooling until the glass is set (the float process).

Method 1, the crown process, was invented early on in human history, probably by the Romans (Figure 3). All flat glass was made by the crown process for hundreds of years until the middle of the nineteenth century, when the process was modified into the manufacture of a large cylinder, to be cut and flattened (Figure 5).

Method 2, continuous forming of a flat sheet, was pioneered by others and not by Pilkington. The flat drawn system that Pilkington adopted was licensed from PPG (Appendix 3, Figures 19–23). Pilkington was very slow to take on flat drawn, as can be read in Chapter 5, and this tardiness nearly bankrupted the company. But method 2, although vastly better than method 1 in terms of quality and cost, did not produce flat glass free of distortion.

The idea of float came to Alastair as he was washing up the dishes after Sunday lunch at his home in Rainhill, near St Helens. His mind was in a relaxed, receptive state. His thinking was, however, still many steps away from the final process, the Holy Grail (method 3).

Alastair asked the question, 'Where in nature do we have perfectly flat surfaces?' The answer, of course, is liquids. So the hunt was on for a liquid which could support molten glass and yet take no part in chemical reaction with it. Tin turned out to be just what was wanted; it has a density greater than glass, plus a low melting point and a high boiling point. Early pilot trials quickly established that the float unit had to have an atmosphere virtually free of oxygen, since tin at around 500°C reacts violently with it. So an atmosphere was created that was a mixture of nitrogen and hydrogen.

The first thinking was to roll the ribbon to perfect planimetry through rollers (a giant water-cooled steel mangle) and then float it on tin to fire-finish the surfaces. The final solution (method 3), of pouring molten glass straight onto the molten tin, was not thought feasible. How would it come out sufficiently flat? How to control the thickness? How would the ribbon be propelled forward on the frictionless tin surface?

Now based in St Helens (the centre of power) and now on the

Pilkington board (the controller of power), Alastair pushed his ideas. A pilot plant (for 24" wide) was soon built, which produced such promising results that the board agreed to go the whole hog and put down a full-scale production unit (for 100" wide). The cost was estimated to be £0.4 million, a large sum for a company whose annual profits were about £3 million.

The full-scale unit was built at four times the estimated cost – £1.6 million in fact. It started up, with much excited anticipation and a certain amount of ceremony, in May 1957. A stable ribbon of glass emerged (even though, as expected, the early glass was a bit of a mess). This was going to be easy. The Holy Grail was within reach.

The bad news was that all the glass from this huge plant, 1,000 tons per week, had to be thrown away. Hour after hour, day after day. None of it was acceptable to the market-place, not one square foot. Remember, the board had stipulated that it had to be of plate quality. The main problem was bubbles in the glass. This was tried, that was tried. Everything was tried in the struggle to make it work, including early experiments with pouring molten glass directly onto molten tin ('direct pour', as it is called). All to no avail – except that direct pour was, in fact, to be the way ...

To say that bubbles were the main problem would be an under-statement. In addition, often the glass had unacceptable levels of distortion, often there were blemishes on the top surface ('top speck', it was called), and often there were blemishes on the bottom surface, or clusters of crystals.

The causes of these faults had to be tracked down and eliminated. Often in solving one problem another was aggravated. Eventually, eleven different causes of top speck were identified, not to mention other faults. This endless hard slog was very demotivating for the team and presented Alastair with a serious leadership challenge.

Summer 1957 went by, autumn went by, Christmas 1957 passed,

Easter 1958 passed, summer 1958 passed. Not one foot of saleable glass! Imagine Alastair's feelings! But Sir Harry Pilkington stayed strong. Harry had unswervingly backed the development and its financing. He was aware from glassmaking history how long new developments take to achieve perfection. Some of his senior colleagues, led by the Research Department, had begun to be seriously doubtful. I think that any negative view of float on the part of those who could foresee some of the difficulties that lay ahead was to some extent justified.

And then, in the autumn of 1958, sixteen months after the start-up, the central two feet of the ribbon cleared, free of all faults. Gradually the centre strip widened, until the whole eight-foot ribbon width was of acceptable quality. At last some saleable glass was being produced. Sixteen months of fruitless, disheartening slog were over. The key question, 'Will it work?', had been triumphantly answered 'Yes!'.

Rejoicing! Success was announced to the world. The major glass-makers of the world came to see it. Apart from the problem of thickness control, Alastair knew how to do it, didn't he? *No! Alastair did not know how to do it!* A new ignorance was about to emerge. What Alastair did not know, at the time, was that a glassmaker had unwittingly broken a key part of the plant, the spout lip. It was that 'mistake' which was the Open Sesame.

Tom Grundy, as manager of the glassmaking team, was there, and in *The Global Miracle of Float Glass* (1990) relates exactly what happened:

> One night, we were fitting a refractory behind the spout lip and squeezing the refractory in position with a long hot iron bar when the bar slipped and cracked the spout, but at the time we did not realise how important it was, because we had raised the spout lip so much on many occasions, changing tiles and the spout was well worn. (pp. 29–30)

The spout, instead of being 'flat', had now become 'U-shaped'.

What was to follow *now* was probably the lowest, most testing time of all. To tell the world that you can do something of such significance and invite them to view it and then, to your horror, discover that you can't repeat the trick was, to say the least, embarrassing.

What had happened was that a certain amount of domestic pride had crept into Alastair's mind. The float plant was not a spick-and-span sight, after all the battles that had been fought by the glassmakers trying every which way to make it work. It looked a mess. Its exterior did not mirror the elegance of what lay within.

A production stoppage had given the opportunity to put the plant back into proper order and replace the broken spout. After the remedial work, the gate was lifted and the molten glass allowed to flow again onto the tin bath with every expectation of a bright future.

'What's happened?' 'What's this?' The ribbon was full of bubbles and devitrification crystals again, just like it had been throughout the slog of the sixteen months during 1957 and 1958.

Direct pour is simple in theory but not in practice. The problem is the highly corrosive nature of molten glass. As molten glass flows over any refractory it is reacting with the refractory, wearing it away, or is stagnant, causing crystals. As the flow of glass wears away the refractory, it reacts chemically with it, causing bubbles and distortion in the finished product. The secret of success is to so arrange the flows that any contamination is directed into the edges.

Figure 15 shows this system of glass flows. I cannot tell you the exact dimensions of the set-up as I do not know them, but I know that to get it to work requires precise positioning. This precise positioning was what had happened as a result of the lucky accident of October 1958, and had caused the process to begin producing good glass.

FLOAT GLASS - DIRECT POUR

2. Good glass flows down the centre, forming a perfect ribbon of finished glass.

1. Molten glass is poured onto a bed of molten tin.

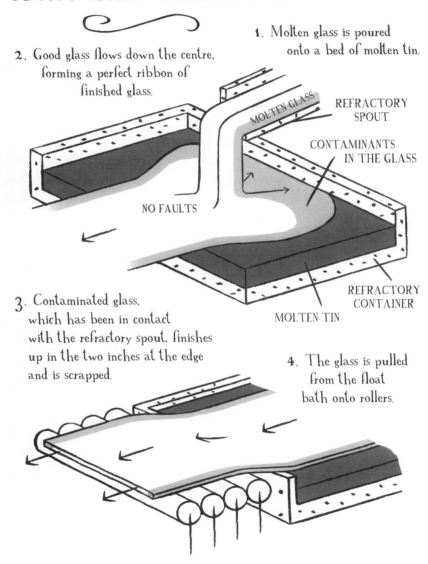

MOLTEN GLASS

REFRACTORY SPOUT

CONTAMINANTS IN THE GLASS

NO FAULTS

REFRACTORY CONTAINER

MOLTEN TIN

3. Contaminated glass, which has been in contact with the refractory spout, finishes up in the two inches at the edge and is scrapped.

4. The glass is pulled from the float bath onto rollers.

Figure 15   Float glass – direct pour

A massive effort ensued, including making a model, using cold materials, of the direct pour process. As a result of this the issue with the spout was revealed, and the solution to the problem built in to the actual glassmaking process.

The quality of the float ribbon was now of sufficient standard for it to be sold for much of the old plate glass trade – shop windows and mirrors, all in $1/4''$ thickness. This was too thick for one significant market – $1/8''$ glass for laminated car windscreens. In order to make a windscreen, one thin ($1/8''$) piece of glass is stuck to a second, similar piece by an intervening layer of plastic, like a sandwich.

This inability of the float process to make thin glass was truly an urgent problem. The Research Department of Pilkington stuck to the answer 'It is impossible'. It is, they said, a law of nature. If the glass is to be perfect, it must go through one stage in the float bath in which it is molten enough to spread on top of the molten tin to form a perfectly flat shiny product. When the molten glass spreads on top of molten tin a phenomenon called surface tension comes into play.

The effect of surface tension is to push (or heap) the molten glass up to $1/4''$ thick. It is in what is called 'equilibrium'. If you do the obvious thing and pull on the ribbon to make it thinner, sure enough it does tend to go thinner, but the edges waist in as well. The surface tension effect fights against the reduction in thickness and tries to heap the molten glass back to $1/4''$ thick. This narrows the ribbon still further, so just pulling on the ribbon is no answer – you finish up with a thread. The problem of how to make thin float seemed intractable.

The eureka moment for thin float occurred when Alastair was having coffee one morning with another engineer, Edward Wood, the son of Charles Wood, the hymn writer, and discussing how to break through this road block. Edward said, 'Why don't you first make a ribbon a quarter of an inch thick on one bath, and then

stretch it on a second bath at a lower temperature where the surface tension effect would be negligible?'

Alastair saw the point immediately, and within two weeks of that
cup of coffee he had achieved $1/8$" thick glass. Float had turned
from an interesting process into a world-beater overnight. (The
result was achieved on one bath, not two.) Alastair had found the
Holy Grail. There was huge relief all round. (Plate 10 shows the
inauguration of the first brand-new float tank, and Plates 11 and
12 the outside and inside of the float bath.)

One other problem remained. How to make glass *thicker* than the
equilibrium thickness, that is, up to two inches thick? The answer
was relatively simple. In order to make a ribbon of thick glass by
the float process, the following apparatus has to be inserted into
the float bath. Carbon restrictor tiles are inserted into the surface
of the tin. These are fixed to each edge of the bath and prevent the
molten glass from spreading down to equilibrium thickness.
These restrictor tiles allow a heavy flow from the spout to pile up
as a thick glass ribbon which cools and sets between the tiles.
Carbon does nor adhere to molten glass, so the thick ribbon can
move down the bath until it is set enough to be lifted off the tin
onto a take-out roller.

From the earliest moment in float's history two major decisions
had come from the top. I do not remember any discussion about
these at formal board meetings, but the principle behind the decisions was obvious:

1. The float process quality must be equal to that of the
    best flat glass available, that is plate glass. Nothing less
    would do.

2. The float process must be licensed to other reputable
    glassmakers. To go it alone would have attracted huge
    attacks from the very people who, in the end, turned
    out to be important supporters and contributors to the
    later development of the process.

Plate 10 Sir Harry Pilkington lighting the first new float tank, 1962

Plate 11 'Alastair's magic box': the float bath in operation

In order to be able to license the idea worldwide, it had to be protected by a strong patent position. Alastair hoped to file a 'full house' of patents – the basic idea, the actual process, and the product. Pilkington was used to patent protection, and already had an existing department to take on this work. First, a search had to be made of all existing patents in the field, and also of appropriate technical literature. Alastair got full patent cover, as he had hoped, in the UK.

He didn't get full cover in the USA. To everybody's amazement a patent of astonishing accuracy was discovered, dated 1902. An American glassmaker had filed a patent describing the float principle – forming a glass ribbon on molten tin. (See Appendix 4 for a detailed description of this.)

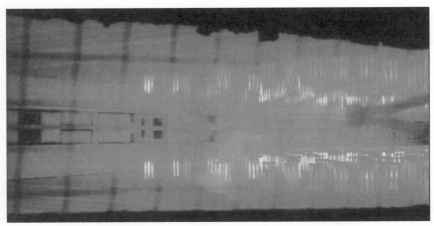

Plate 12 Inside the float bath (from Barker 1994)

This patent stood in Alastair's way. It was the only time Alastair was heard to swear. 'This guy just sat in his armchair. *We've* bloody done it. There must be something that is new and patentable in our process.' Of course there was, and stronger patents emerged as a result, all based on the principle of direct pour. Problems continued to be encountered, but they were no longer fundamental, and from this moment on the royalties rolled in, soon reaching around £20 million per year. Accolades also continued to flow in, with citations from all areas of the world, a knighthood, and what Alastair regarded as his highest accolade, 'FRS' – Fellow of the Royal Society.

Alastair's great contribution to the company and the nation did not end with the success of float. He followed Sir Harry as chairman and set up what seemed to be a very successful triumvirate at the top of the company. Alastair as the chairman appointed two deputy chairmen under him. One was Leslie Wall, who was originally a lawyer but had developed into someone who had a good grasp of the totality of the business. He was crucial to the commercial success of float through designing the licences and determining how the float improvements would be handled. The third member was John Leighton Boyce, who had joined the company late in his career. His strengths were finance and also, surprisingly, people.

Alastair continued to invent. It was largely his influence which caused a system to be set up of siphoning off the profits to encourage seedling businesses. Float caused a reduction in the labour force; the profits from float helped (indirectly) to create new jobs. He was a founder member of Business in the Community. He set up a much-valued scheme for teaching prizes for the Cambridge University dons and lecturers. These were cash prizes given to the best teachers chosen by the combined votes of their bosses, peers and pupils.

The directors of Pilkington at the time of the early commercial success of float are shown in Plate 13. Plate 14 shows the team of people who were actually physically involved with – and indeed at daily risk of physical injury from – the glassmaking process. We cannot, however, end this part of the story without paying tribute to a third group of people, the brains who struggled to overcome the many technical barriers. It would be invidious to name them because equally important were the efforts of the glassmakers who had to implement, under hot, dangerous working conditions, changes to the plant that the brains recommended.

Plate 13   Sir Harry Pilkington with executive directors, 1968

Looking back on the whole saga of trying to tame the float process, Alastair was to write in 1976, 'If we had been aware of the horrors which were to come, it is unlikely that we would have proceeded with development work.'

That somewhat illogical statement gives a flavour of what the developers and their backers had had to contend with. Alastair, and his team of young engineers, glassmakers and scientists, were working at the forefront of technology. Nobody (literally nobody) in the outside world was able to tell the team the answers to most of their problems. Of course they gave support, but the team had had to crack their problems by their own creativity, working at all times beyond the limit of their knowledge and experience.

Plate 14   Sir Alastair Pilkington's team of glassmakers

Chapter Twelve

Rebellion: The 1970 Strike

For a number of years before the 1970 strike hit, we knew that all was not well with our people. Something was 'hurting'. Perhaps we (the top management) suffered from hubris as we basked in the brightness of float's success. Float had been launched on the world a decade before, and with licensing gathering momentum substantial royalties had flowed into the company coffers by 1970. We were expanding, and we had to look beyond the traditional boundaries of St Helens for our enlarging workforce – people who were from a different tribe and 'knew not' Pilk's and St Helens.

Also, we had neglected the needs of our people. Perhaps we had been sidetracked by the loyalty and dedication of those at all levels who had worked on float. All of them, from top to bottom, had put in long hours, had performed beyond the call of duty, had struggled and solved the endless technical problems that float kept throwing at them.

Senior management still stuck to the view that they knew what was best for their people. There, however, 'straws in the wind' which alerted us to the fact that something was not right. Many of the bonus schemes were no longer working as originally intended; there was a lack of fairness in the way in which people were rewarded; there a rash of incidents (work-to-rules, go-slows, strikes); life was no longer rewarding for the management trying to cope with a rebellious spirit pervading their people. One of the middle managers said to me, 'I want out. Being a manager is no longer fun.'

On the other hand, some companies, like ICI and Shell, had instituted new ways of managing which were intriguing and appeared to be effective. The Japanese industry had developed ways of involving the shop floor in the management of industrial units. Volvo was experimenting with self-organising units building an individual car from start to finish. These ideas were aimed at involving the workforce in new ways of managing.

So, in those pre-strike days, encouraged by such ideas the Pilkington management took an initiative to set up a wide-ranging review of the company's productivity. This review was called the Productivity Programme. It was widely announced throughout the company and had the support of the trade unions.

About this time, a shop steward bumped into me in the street just outside one of the works:

'David, trouble's brewing. The tom-toms are beating.'

'What can we do, Harry? – we've started the Productivity Programme.'

'Well, you had better get on with it!'

The Productivity Programme was set up in 1968, two years before the strike. We decided to work with Professor Lupton of Manchester Business School (MBS), who would be able to provide extra resources and a theoretical background to the work, as well as successful examples of how others were approaching industrial problems in new ways.

It was decided at that time to use one of the five St Helens works as a test bed where any new thinking could be tried out. The works chosen was Ravenhead (significantly not making flat glass, and therefore rather 'safer' in top management's mind).

Professor Lupton introduced us to the 'systems approach'. This approach works on the principle that everything which occurs in a works is, in some way, interconnected. The key is to understand not only what the interconnections are, but also which are the most important. (Analysis, rather than jumping to conclusions.) MBS had developed ways of mapping any system once it had been understood. Such maps, once agreed by the parties concerned (shop-floor workers, foremen, shop stewards, management), can be used to develop improvements. They can also be stored, kept up to date and used to trace the consequences of any future decisions.

A small team of experienced managers from all over the company, representing diverse professional disciplines, were released from their normal duties. The first step this team took was to have a period of introspection (team building) while they thought about how they were going to approach the job.

Some aspects of the system were clearly unimportant. For instance, there would be no point in measuring the height of the chimneys or counting the works' cats. On the other hand, some senior influences in the company were already quite clear about what needed looking at: 'examine the bonus schemes or, better still, union restrictive practices'. MBS pointed out that it would be unproductive to examine these in isolation from other, interrelated factors which might be more important, for example management style. Were management too authoritarian? Did they listen? Was there a robust system of communication with the shop floor?

During this time of introspection the team also worked with MBS on the theory and practice of how to manage change, how to conduct investigation of social issues, how to design an organisation. In this way the careful and methodical work of the Productivity Programme was begun.

However, as often happens to the 'best-laid plans', our plans were knocked awry and were overtaken by the strike, but the basic idea of the systems approach was to come into its own in a different way. While the crisis created by the strike was urgently dealt with by works management, the Productivity Programme provided a think tank made up of people who could stay cool and calm away from the noise and smoke of battle.

The first I heard of the strike was while I was on holiday in Switzerland. I had come down to the village of Zermatt from skiing on the glacier under the Matterhorn to be told that I was to ring St Helens. It was Sir Harry: 'There's a bit of a panic on here. They're all out. You'd better come home.'

Within 48 hours, I was back in St Helens and straight into meetings with management, and then with union people. Everybody was at sea, including the trade unions. What are they striking about? Nobody could give a clear answer; all we could do was to repeat the mantra 'We do not negotiate under duress' or, to put it clearly, 'They must return to work before they can get any advantage from going on strike'.

I was the director responsible for industrial relations, and also chairman of all the negotiating bodies. I was at the epicentre of this earthquake. I was floundering. We were all floundering. And so it continued for nearly three weeks.

During these three weeks, so serious had matters become that Lord Cooper, the general secretary of the National Union of General and Municipal Workers (NUGMW), visited St Helens. He wanted to talk with the directors. He didn't come to negotiate. His message seemed to be 'They will come back. Most of them don't want to be on strike, sense will prevail. They will not go out again.'

The union had refused to make the strike official. It offered the strikers hardship money, which was less than strike pay. So, the union was giving out the same message as the company: 'Return to work, and then we will open negotiations.' It had lost control of its members. It had around eight thousand members in

St Helens, all of whom were idle.

According to Lane and Roberts' book *Strike at Pilkington's*, the strike was really aimed at unseating the union. Such an objective had already been achieved at Ford's Merseyside plant. If this is true, then the union was relatively powerless in the situation.

About two weeks into the strike an unofficial leadership committee had been set up. It was, in fact, the birth of an unaffiliated union which steadily gathered power, claiming around three thousand Pilkington members at its peak. It was called the Glass and General Workers Union (GGWU).

It was at this time that I received a telephone call which was to change everything:

> 'Hello, David, this is Tom.'
>
> 'How are you, Tom?'
>
> 'David, listen. You have lost the initiative. You have got to do something.'

It was Tom Chapman on the phone. I had met him at Christian industrial conferences and had great respect for him, an ex-trade union leader who now worked for the Archbishop of Canterbury. Tom had told me before about his 'storm troopers', trained to go into the heart of strikes in order to establish what the real issues are and then attempt to build bridges between the parties concerned:

> 'Will you meet a group of my people who have been living in St Helens for the last week? They will tell you what to do. Tomorrow, Saturday afternoon, at your home.'

Into my home the next day came six men. They were all professional people, including a doctor, a stockbroker, and a researcher at the National Physical Laboratory, who had given up a week of their time to live in the town. They had gone round the pubs and clubs and listened. The message was simple: 'You must make a cash offer early next week and the amount has to be £3.' This was breathtaking: £3 per week on the existing wage of £15! This was a pay rise of 20 per cent. No strings attached. Unprecedented, but they explained that the offer had to be generous, beyond doubt acceptable to the strikers, in order to ensure a clean return to work. 'There are people involved in this strike who do not ever want a settlement.'

The next step was obvious. Sir Harry Pilkington had to be contacted and convinced. 'Does he go to church? – we will waylay him.' And they did! The six, Sir Harry and I all met at Windle Hall, Sir Harry's house, the next day, on Sunday afternoon and the argument for the £3 rise was put. Sir Harry saw the point immediately. There and then he telephoned round the board and arranged a meeting at 9 a.m. the next morning. By a happy coincidence the timing was good – there was a scheduled meeting of the Joint Industrial Council, the main negotiating body, that very Monday afternoon.

Such was Sir Harry's command, that once he was convinced the rest of the board quickly came into line. Next came the difficult part – 'turning the heads' of the senior management concerned (about seven people). The turning of heads was from 'We will not negotiate under duress' to 'Here is £3 for you'. That was cruel. One of the seven managers said to me afterwards, 'Don't ever do that again.' It was brutal behaviour towards the senior management. The senior manager responsible for industrial relations under me died of a heart attack within a few weeks.

The offer of £3 was put, on the Monday afternoon, to the union at the Joint Industrial Council. The union accepted it, but two mass meetings of the strikers on the Tuesday and again on the Friday of that week rejected it. A breakaway union had been formed. The strike went on for a further three weeks.

A detailed analysis of what occurred is provided by Lane and Roberts' *Strike at Pilkington's*. Eventually, after a 'parsons ballot' (a vote organised by all the churches in St Helens), which favoured a return to work, and after a promised intervention by Vic Feather, General Secretary of the TUC, there was a complete return to work on 20 May 1970.

That wasn't the end of the matter. The breakaway union, the GGWU, had to gain official recognition from the company to achieve viability. An issue arose involving a member of the union and a meeting with management was demanded by that member, who was to be accompanied by a GGWU official. By this means the union could gain recognition.

The company (with the backing of the official union, the NUGMW) knew how to prevent recognition – the meeting was refused. The GGWU called a second strike. It was an exciting moment. It claimed thousands of paid-up members (it probably had around 2,500 out of the total of 8,000).

The senior management waited anxiously. How many would walk out? In the event only around five hundred went on strike a second time. The threat evaporated. More than that, the situation allowed the opportunity to dismiss the ringleaders of the strike who had identified themselves by eventually refusing to return to work.

You might imagine that, once the strikers were back at work and full glass production resumed, all would be calm. Not a bit of it! The first task was the absorption of the £3 into the wage structure. The work required to effect this was taken on by the management of one of the works – Float Works. The other employees, maintenance, transport, staff, had to be treated in an equal manner in order to maintain fairness. The grievances procedure had to be revived. A mountain of work was to be undertaken.

Beyond this there was a 'velvet rebellion' going on – a wholesale peaceful movement demanding change which we had not envisaged before the strike. The velvet revolution was something of a surprise. We had not expected to find such pressure from groups of employees who were traditionally close to top management – staff and foremen. The pressure was for a formal channel to represent their views through a trade union. Even more of a surprise was to find that the 'junior' levels of management (those above the foremen) were similarly minded, though in this case a jointly designed internal channel sufficed.

The Productivity Programme was beefed up by the addition of more people, senior company management drafted in from their normal jobs. As well as helping with the work going on at the centre on wage structures, each major works had its own team, under the control of the individual works manager, to examine its own needs.

In order to reflect the larger role of the Productivity Programme, a more appropriate and widely recognised name was given to the work, 'organisational development'. What is organisational development exactly? There are a number of definitions. It is the application of the systems approach to every aspect of the company's existence. It is the ability to question everything. It is the freedom to go anywhere, see anything, think the unthinkable and (on returning to base) say the unsayable.

In more practical terms, it is helping the management to address fully the issues which are actually holding up progress. These issues are talked through by everyone involved – management, foremen, the shop floor, shop stewards. Sometimes the answer falls out readily, but usually matters are rather more complex (otherwise they would have been solved already!). This is where tools, like a map of the systems, are helpful. The map can be committed to paper after all involved agree with it.

One participant in an OD team told me, excitedly, that working in this way was 'Christianity in action'. I suppose that if it is possible to map all the significant connections within a system, and if the team is given the time and resources to do this and train the active management in the methods used, some kind of leap forward ought to be possible. It is, after all, application of the golden rule, 'Do as you would be done by'.

Perhaps, as one of the leaders of the OD work, I lacked sufficient faith in the ideas and lacked sufficient commitment to push them through. I have to confess that I was disappointed with the outcome. It did not change the Pilkington management style in a root-and-branch way. One of the things we learned from MBS was how hard it is to effect such a change.

Not all that was achieved convinced our hard-headed senior production managers. At a meeting arranged to try to explain what we were about, such a manager said to one of the OD team leaders, 'John, I thought that you were a down-to-earth production man.' Some ideas, however, did stick:

1.   The understanding that everybody is pursuing a strategy that makes sense to them. Nobody wakes up in the morning and says to themselves 'Today I will be awkward'.

2.   If any problems are fully discussed with all those involved and joint solutions reached, the likelihood of a successful outcome is high.

3.   Choosing solutions to problems has always involved a balance between cost and effectiveness, but one should aim first for the solution that (a) costs the least and (b) has the highest chance of success. By this approach confidence between those concerned is built up. This is the win–win way.

4.   Decision-making should, as far as possible, be decentralised and pushed down as near to the workface as possible.

A joint review by MBS and the OD team of whether they had been successful concluded that on some sites the achievement was real. Costs were reduced, the quality of the product improved, manpower used more effectively, labour turnover reduced, better relations between management and employees achieved.

Such results were measurable, but not always in financial terms (unlike float, whose success was obvious and unarguable). Success in the human field tends to be vague and ephemeral. Certain sites were unconvinced of the new thinking and stuck to the old ways of managing.

Some major elements arising from the OD work were universally adopted. No longer were arbitrary decisions by management allowed. Everything had to be discussed among all those involved, all options for change considered, and conclusions jointly agreed. Decisions were to be announced first by management, never to be learned first from the media or the trade unions. If a decision involved workers becoming redundant, there had to be a policy for it to be voluntary. If such a voluntary policy was unlikely to be sufficient, a special payment might be made. Action was taken to decentralise decision-making, pushing decisions as near as possible to the workforce (against considerable resistance from the top!).

And what about the strike? What did it achieve? One clear result, a £3 pay increase for everyone! It inadvertently opened up and brought forward some previously hidden forces, such as a desire on the part of the staff (and foremen) for unionisation, and a desire on the part of middle management for an improved relationship with the board. It opened the path to the new and better management style of involving all those affected by a problem in its solution.

The strike and its aftermath forced an upgrade by Pilkington of its policy of treating its people with decency and consideration. The strike had opened the windows and allowed a blast of fresh air to blow through the company.

The OD team was finally dissolved. Its members then returned to their previous jobs or to similar ones, and, in some cases, to promotion. Thus the experience of working in OD was grafted back onto work in normal jobs, sometimes successfully and sometimes less so.

Chapter Thirteen

The Sale of the Birthright

After 145 years of a profitable, stable and expanding business, why did the family decide to sell out?

The period leading up to the sale in 1970 had been extremely successful. The flat glass market was expanding rapidly, with Pilkington as a flourishing participant. The company had invented the perfect way to make flat glass and its float process was rapidly becoming accepted worldwide as the only manufacturing method.

The level of float royalties was growing and often doubled the profits from trading. Dr Johnson's thoughts on the sale of Thrale's brewery – '... the potentiality of growing rich beyond the dreams of avarice' – could qually well be applied to Pilkington. So, why sell when the company stood on such a glorious threshold?

The case for cashing in such a promising birthright had to be a strong one. In fact, it had many facets which, in combination, built up to an inevitability.

Although I was a director of the company, I do not recall any discussion of this major change. David Bricknell, who has made a search of company files and board minutes, has failed to find anything recorded. It seems as if Sir Harry Pilkington made up his mind and so it happened. No doubt he talked it over with other directors, the bigger family shareholders and financial experts within and without the company.

What were the issues which tolled the death knell of this great family business? There is no doubt that it was a death. It was the end of the Glass Act with its long-term views, its noble (unwritten) values and its blood cohesion. Life after 1970 was to be different. The owners of the company were now from the outside world and the company had to conform to this world. Business was moving fast to the triumph of capitalism that marked the end of the twentieth century, with its emphasis of short-termism, sometimes labelled 'get rich – quick'.

What were the issues that were building up to the inevitability of a public sale? The one that stands out most clearly was the loss of the category under which the business operated, Exempt Private Company. This special status was withdrawn by the Government in 1962. From then on, the company had to lodge its accounts at Companies House. In other words, its turnover, its profits, became public knowledge.

The loss of Exempt Private Company status and the flotation on the Stock Exchange are fully discussed in Bricknell's (2009) book (pp. 21, 82), and I am indebted to his research in this area. Bricknell notes that, although there is no recorded board minute or other papers on this issue, Sir Harry decided in the early 1960s that the company would have to go public and the date of 1970 was chosen. Once a loss of company secrecy had occurred, one of the main commercial reasons for remaining private had gone. That secrecy was a key element in the speed and the completeness that accompanied the development and exploitation of the float process.

There were other tides pointing to the sale of the birthright. One such was the waning interest of the younger generation of the family in the company. Only two members of the fifth generation showed serious interest, Antony, who eventually became chairman, and Hector, who held a senior management position but not a board appointment. In addition all the family had moved south. The only member who lived north of the Mersey was David, the author, who continued there until his retirement.

There was one event that caused two of the fifty to travel north to St Helens. This was the company's AGM, when its shareholders had the right to call the directors to account. The two were Robin and Bill, members of the fourth generation, both active in the city and primed to ask pertinent questions.

The meeting took place in the formality of the boardroom. The directors sat around a horseshoe table, as was their wont at a board meeting, very solemn – it was like being in church. The two shareholders sat 'below the salt' (Figure 16). It took some courage, not helped by the seating plan, to ask the difficult questions, Sir Harry in the chair trying, like all company chairmen, to get through his agenda as quickly and in as pain-free a way as possible.

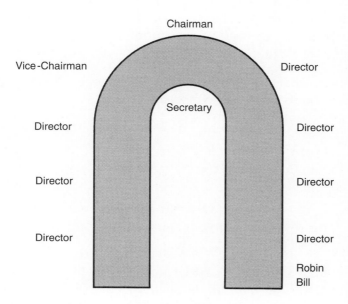

Figure 16   The board table

Robin and Bill, determined to get their just time allocation, kept the questioning going for at least fifteen minutes (more if possible). Sir Harry started applying the brakes soon, after ten minutes, with increasing irritation! After the shareholders' vote of thanks, the 'two' departed, to rejoin the meeting at lunch. The directors were glad to be able to get on with the real business.

The ethos of secrecy partly accounted for this tetchiness (later continued under Sir Antony Pilkington). It was an ancient tradition of glassmakers to guard their secrets jealously. It was of huge commercial advantage. Even the board members only got the accounts two weeks before and had to hand them back at the board meeting.

The other powerful tide running against the idea of a family business was the rising price of the shares. Although Pilkington was a private company the value of its shares was set annually by the Inland Revenue. So, if any family shareholder wished to sell, it was becoming more and more difficult to find a buyer (who had to be among the 50). This was not helpful when the coming of float pointed to the need to raise more capital for the expected exploitation of float and the resultant company expansion.

There were other ways of solving the need for fresh capital which, no doubt, Sir Harry explored:

1.   Take out long-term loans from finance houses such as insurance companies (i.e. repeat what happened in the 1920s, when Pilkington took a loan from the Prudential).

2.   Find a wealthy partner (i.e. 'marry' someone looking for diversification, e.g. a chemical company, or a fuel supplier).

3.   Find a wealthy partner in the glass industry like the American Corning Glass, or, as eventually happened some thirty years later, a Japanese glassmaker.

The solution that emerged was the one we know: float the company on the Stock Exchange. The family had reached the point where the birthright had to be sold. The sale would be to the general public via the Stock Exchange and so give access to unlimited capital. And so, the deed was done. The Glass Act reached its end; the Pilkington family relationship with glass had run its course.

Chapter Fourteen

The Fifth Generation: Antony Pilkington's Watch (1980–1995)

The fifth generation was unable to hold on to what the fourth had already in effect lost. The birthright, the 170 years of symbiotic relationship between the Pilkingtons and glass, was ended. Pilkington was now a public company. Fiscal and financial pressures, coupled with historical movements, were making the old close-knit family business an impossibility. So the Pilkingtons were not to be blamed. They were forced to make the sale. As we will see, however, there is argument about how they effected it.

In the past, Pilkington had had the advantage of fiscal systems which allowed the company accounts to be kept secret except to a very select band of people. The UK tax authorities obviously were aware in order to calculate the normal company Corporation Tax burden, but also to calculate the value of Pilkington's shares.

The other part of the select band were the company shareholders – 50 in total, who were all family members. The technical description of the company was Exempt Private Company. Fiscal policy was changing and such a category was no longer allowed. Pilkington could still remain owned by only 50 shareholders, but its accounts now had to be published.

Once the company accounts were in the public domain, the City of London rottweilers could start to sink their teeth into them.

Critical comment on performance started to emerge, but perhaps more influential was the ability of the market pundits to work out the value of a Pilkington share. (This was about three times the value officially established by the tax authorities.) Pilkington family shareholders, the 50, could now see clearly the value of their birthright, and of the sacrifices they had made over the years in supporting the policy of ploughing back the profits. The long-term views of their forefathers were now to be seriously challenged by younger family members who no longer lived near, or worked in, or cared about, St Helens, and whose loyalty to the old values was diminishing fast.

It is difficult to write about the closing moments of the Glass Act. Are we writing a history or an obituary? It is all a bit messy. Like all endings there will be a mixture of the bitter and the sweet, with much remaining to be resolved as more hindsight is available.

Looking back, the real ending was the selling of the birthright in 1970. We all knew, at the time, that 1970 was a significant moment, but just how significant it was can only now be judged.

If we had realised then what we know now, we should have held the world's largest party (or wake) for all those who had participated in the Glass Act, all those still alive enjoying a proper celebration of our joint achievement. Finish the Glass Act with a bang. Of course, such an event would have been impossible for many reasons, not least of which was that we would not have known at that time to whom we were handing over our heritage.

There was no discussion, that I remember, about what might happen next. Should the family have hung together and at least have retained control for a period? Should a proper 'For Sale' notice have been erected to sound out possible suitors on a worldwide basis? Antony did try to reduce the haemorrhaging of family shareholders, but to no avail.

As a result of not properly reading the runes, the company continued in much the same way as before. The only change was that the share price now took precedence over the Test Match cricket score at lunchtime discussions. The world outside Pilkington was changing rapidly. The company continued in the same way, but it could never be the same. The company continued to have a Pilkington as chairman. Alastair, the hero of the climax of the Glass Act, naturally followed Harry as chairman, the question of whether he was a family member or not having faded into the distance. He was accepted as a member of the fourth generation.

But when it came to the fifth generation, did it matter that the Pilkington momentum continued unquestioned? I think it did matter. Antony, as the senior member of the fifth generation, was handed a poisoned chalice when he was appointed to the chair. The sustaining soul of Pilkington had melted away. It was unfair to push Antony into the chair without the right informed debate. As confirmation of this take on Antony's chairmanship, at the end of his first year in office he had to report that the UK operation as a whole had made the first loss since 1923. If, however, the full record of profits from Antony's innings is set out and a certain period chosen, he did have a short, golden spell. It wasn't to last.

It must be said that Antony was an astute businessman. By great skill, he won the Scandinavian market from Saint-Gobain, and Pilkington established the first float line in that territory, at Halmstad in 1976. At the same time, he had to preside over the final stages of the exploitation of float worldwide. The licence for the process had to be completed in all the territories worldwide, which sometimes involved great difficulties. (The Chinese licence required over ten visits to Shanghai.) But a new source of revenue (and much work for Pilkington people) emerged, in that many of our licensees were much less skilled than Pilkington in the melting of the glass, and so we were asked to upgrade them in the area of technology.

One of the great foundations of the Pilkington saga had been long-term views. Short-termism, as exemplified by the bid from 'British Tyre & Rubber' (BTR), was now the real power behind business. Short-termism overwhelmed Pilkington.

Antony had no benefit from the old cohesion of blood relationships, which now became a burden. In fact, Antony told David Bricknell (who was at that time company secretary, and naturally rather intimate with the chairman) that he had felt the pressure of the preceding four generations of the family during the BTR bid. (He didn't want to be the one who gave the company away.) He felt deeply his role as Trustee of the company, in that he was the custodian of the company for the future.

If you ask the question 'Did Antony enjoy being chairman?', the answer was that he enjoyed the battle against BTR. In this battle he was masterful, he was magnificent. Why? Because the pressures he felt he was under from the preceding four generations provided him with the unchanging and unquestioning war cry, 'The company is *not* for sale!' In this he was supported by management, employees, trade unions, MPs, and the community of St Helens. The battle concluded in BTR withdrawing its bid. Antony had won.

Another great challenge which Antony faced was from the powerful American licensee PPG, which challenged the very basis of the licence – the validity of the patents. The full story of this challenge is well covered and described in David Bricknell's outstanding book *Float: Pilkingtons' glass revolution*.

Just as with the BTR bid, this challenge to float was a battle that had to be won. The integrity of the float licensing was essential to whoever owned the company.

Big money was involved. Antony was now into a legal battle – top lawyers were involved and mounting legal fees – but more important than that was the security of the existing stream of licensing income pouring into the company coffers: £20 million per annum from 80 float plants worldwide, and with the potential of more being built with great regularity. (There was also in the background a possible criminal charge against the company under US law, on the legal grounds that Pilkington had mis-sold the Float Licence.)

The world watched this legal battle with great attention. All licensees would be glad to be relieved of having to pay their dues, although the cost of a licence was not that onerous to anyone who knew their glassmaking.

It was an American company that led the charge – PPG, the Western world's most powerful flat glass maker. Why PPG took it into their heads to mount such a challenge is interesting. There was certainly some misplaced pride involved. Was there some misplaced animosity? Bricknell notes that the chairman of PPG did not like Antony.

To his credit, Antony won the battle with PPG. Pilkington continued to license the world. The patents were never challenged in court. However, the cost of defending the patents was huge – £60 million.

In the historical optic the BTR battle assumes an interesting aspect. Under the optic of the old, the answer was clear and Antony gave it: 'The company is not for sale.' Under the optic of the new, the answer to BTR might have been different:

1. The company *is* for sale – but not to you, BTR.

2. Before this sale is accomplished, however, the Pilkington family will retain control until …

3. … a worldwide search for a suitable successor has been completed.

The fourth generation missed this opportunity. It wasn't until after the fifth generation that such an opportunity arose. The takeover by a Japanese company, Nippon Sheet Glass, appears to be a fulfilment of the above scenario. Could it have been realised earlier? Unclear.

The fifth generation had a difficult passage. There is much more that could be written about the difficulties of the world in which Antony had to lead. In the early '80s the company was making trading losses in the UK. (Input from float licensing covered these losses.) Competition was intense, much stoked by licensees coming on stream with more up-to-date plant than Pilkington's.

Antony probably had the most difficult of any of the chairman-ships of the company. Manpower had to be reduced massively: 20 per cent of the managers, including senior management, were made redundant. Many of the initiatives in diversification had to be sold off or abandoned. The trade unions were vocal and powerful. It was retrenchment back to the primary product, flat glass.

Antony had a chief executive under him who had not grown up in the Pilkington stable. The board contained powerful independents. The direction in which the company should move was less clear-cut. All competitors could now make perfect glass. The old battles over choice of technology were a thing of the past. Criticism of company policy from outside pundits was sharper and more vociferous. Everybody was now only interested in the half-year profits. The long-term future was disdained. This, in my view, may have been the reason why insufficient thought was given to a possible partnership with Corning.

Short-termism was now the reality behind business. Short-termism overwhelmed Pilkington, short-termism, arguably, overwhelmed Antony. He died prematurely in 2000, aged 65, after a short retirement.

Perhaps I have presented rather a rosy view of the Pilkingtons and the kind of capitalism they represented. Perhaps a certain amount of ego shows, in thinking that I was working for a noble enterprise. For an antidote to this view, read Lane and Roberts' impressive book *Strike at Pilkington's*, a scholarly account written from a socialist perspective.

I have to confess, I am proud to have been part of the Pilkington dynasty and the Glass Act. I am proud to have been nicknamed 'Group Chief Communist'.

References

Barker, Theo (1977) *The Glassmakers: Pilkington: the rise of an international company 1826–1976* (London: Weidenfeld & Nicolson).

Barker, Theo (1994) *Pilkington: An age of glass: the illustrated history* (London: Boxtree).

Bricknell, David (2009) *Float: Pilkingtons' glass revolution* (Lancaster: Crucible).

Grundy, Tom (1990) *The Global Miracle of Float Glass* (Haydock, St Helens: Tom Grundy).

Lane, Tony and Roberts, Kenneth (1971) *Strike at Pilkington's* (London: Fontana/Collins).

Williams-Ellis, Elizabeth (1997) *The Pilkington Story* (St Ouen, Jersey: Elizabeth Williams-Ellis).

Appendix 1   Millennial Timeline

Figure 17 shows the development of glassmaking from earliest times up to the present day. The major glassmaking methods are described more fully in the text and the accompanying figures.

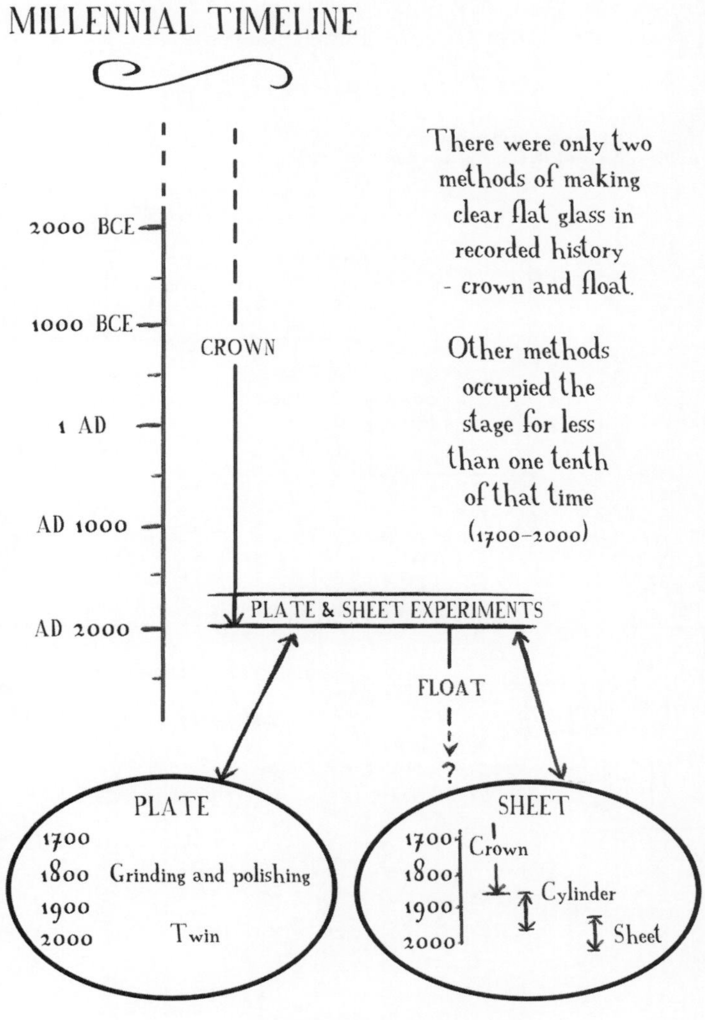

MILLENNIAL TIMELINE

There were only two methods of making clear flat glass in recorded history - crown and float.

Other methods occupied the stage for less than one tenth of that time (1700-2000)

2000 BCE

1000 BCE

CROWN

1 AD

AD 1000

AD 2000

PLATE & SHEET EXPERIMENTS

FLOAT

?

PLATE

1700
1800   Grinding and polishing
1900
2000   Twin

SHEET

1700   Crown
1800
1900   Cylinder
2000   Sheet

Figure 17   Millennial timeline

Appendix 2   Pilkington Family Tree

Figure 18 presents a simplified Pilkington family tree, citing company members by their commonly used names. For reasons of space it omits Alastair Pilkington (see p. 97), and Hector Vere Pilkington, great-great-grandson of 'Go-getter' William. Helen Rosemary Cozens-Hardy, shown here as wife of Douglas Phelps, was also sister of Peter Cozens-Hardy (see Figure 7).

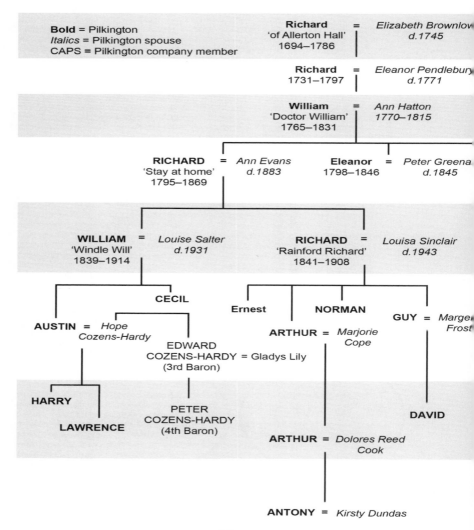

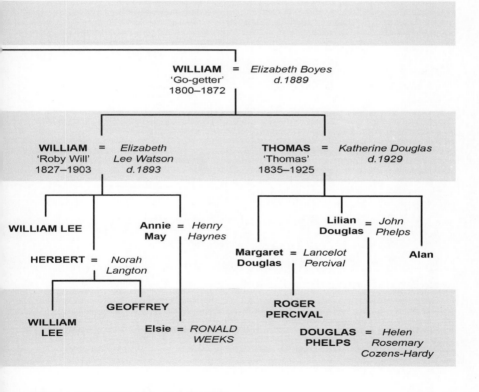

Figure 18   Pilkington family tree

Appendix 3   Flat Drawn

The term 'flat drawn' has been used in this text to describe three ways of making a ribbon of clear transparent flat glass directly from molten glass. Flat drawn works on the basic idea of dipping a knife in treacle (Figure 19).

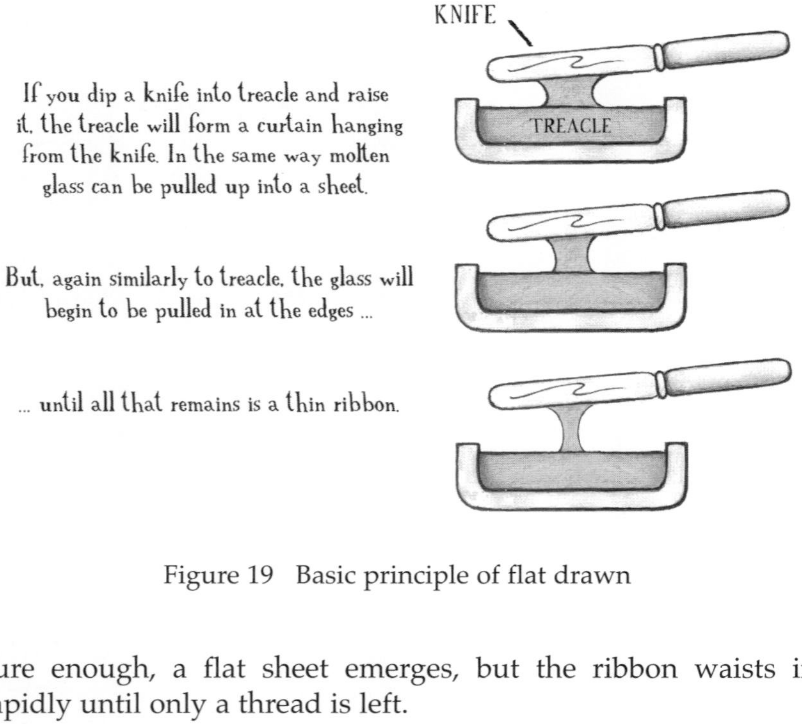

If you dip a knife into treacle and raise it, the treacle will form a curtain hanging from the knife. In the same way molten glass can be pulled up into a sheet.

But, again similarly to treacle, the glass will begin to be pulled in at the edges ...

... until all that remains is a thin ribbon.

Figure 19   Basic principle of flat drawn

Sure enough, a flat sheet emerges, but the ribbon waists in rapidly until only a thread is left.

How to prevent this waisting? Only three commercial methods of keeping the width were ever discovered, Colburn, Fourcault and PPG. Colburn is illustrated in Figure 20.

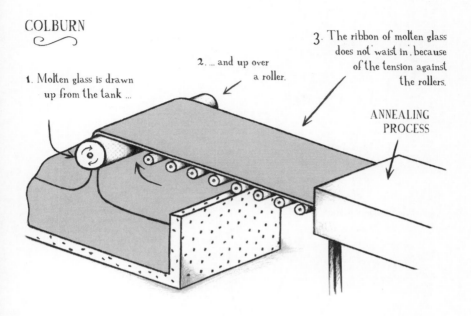

COLBURN

1. Molten glass is drawn
up from the tank ...

2. ... and up over
a roller.

3. The ribbon of molten glass
does not waist in, because
of the tension against
the rollers.

ANNEALING
PROCESS

Figure 20   Colburn

The problem here is that bending the glass over the roller spoils its pristine surface. Fourcault (Figure 21) also suffers from a weakness, which is that drawing the glass through a slot spoils its surface.

So the problem remains – how to draw a ribbon straight from the molten glass without spoiling the pristine surface? The answer is shown in Figure 22.

FOURCAULT

1. A ceramic boat called a 'debiteuse' is pushed down into molten glass.

3. ... and the molten glass is drawn away upwards through rollers.

2. The molten glass flows up through a slot in the debiteuse owing to a difference in pressures ...

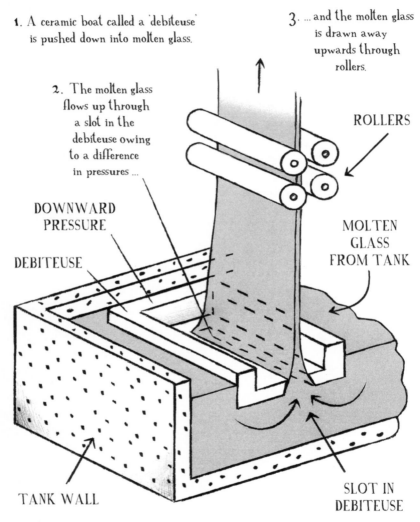

ROLLERS

DOWNWARD PRESSURE

MOLTEN GLASS FROM TANK

DEBITEUSE

TANK WALL

SLOT IN DEBITEUSE

Figure 21   Fourcault

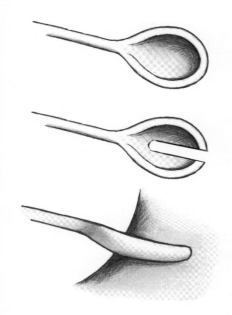

Take a ladle (pictured here from above).

Cut a slot in the ladle and fit it around the edge of the molten glass ribbon as it first rises from the glass.

The ladle will cool the edges of the glass sufficiently and the edge holds!

Figure 22   The idea behind PPG

The working process is shown in full in Figure 23.

Flat drawn is to be distinguished from three other ways of making clear, transparent flat glass: crown (Figure 3, p. 17); plate (grinding and polishing) (Figure 8, p. 35); and float (casting molten glass onto molten tin (Figure 15, p. 116).

'Old Faithful' crown, with its 3,000-year history as the only way of making a piece of clear flat glass, became a relic in the nineteenth century. All other processes became obsolete in the latter half of the twentieth century when float became the only way.

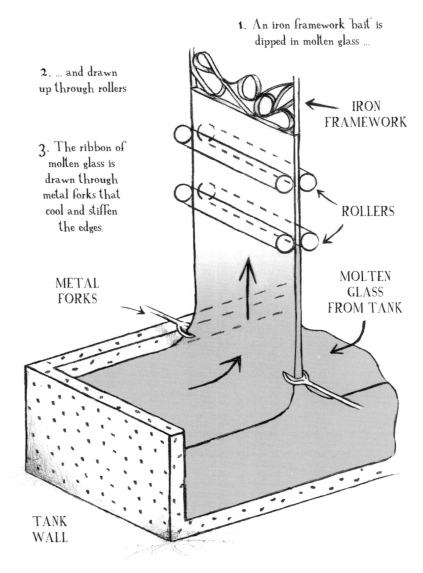

1. An iron framework 'bait' is dipped in molten glass ...

2. ... and drawn up through rollers

3. The ribbon of molten glass is drawn through metal forks that cool and stiffen the edges.

IRON FRAMEWORK

ROLLERS

METAL FORKS

MOLTEN GLASS FROM TANK

TANK WALL

Figure 23   PPG

Appendix 4   The Heal Patent

The Heal patent (granted in 1902) caused Alastair to swear: 'Heal just sat in an armchair and dreamt it up. *We've* bloody done it!'

The Heal patent (Figure 24) could not have worked. There were a number of reasons for this, only the chief of which are given here. Heal knew nothing about the 'key'. Alastair had found the key to the float process by mistake (p. 114). The molten glass has to be delivered onto the tin by means of a spout, which gives a thick, narrow flow that is allowed to fall without interference onto the tin. The flow that occurs from this arrangement puts any faults emanating from the spout into the edges of the ribbon.

A second reason Heal would have failed is that the molten glass from the spout has to be allowed to flow freely from the spout area and down the bath free of any constriction, in order to allow the molten glass to establish equilibrium thickness. A third reason for failure is that the bath has to be virtually hermetically sealed against the ingress of air (oxygen).

In addition, the bath must have a second form of defence to deal with any air (oxygen) that does penetrate the bath. This defence is piped nitrogen and hydrogen. Nitrogen and hydrogen put the bath atmosphere into pressure as well as mopping up any air (oxygen). For this function to be carried out, both gases are required in large, continuously piped quantities, and in 1902 these were not available anywhere in the world.

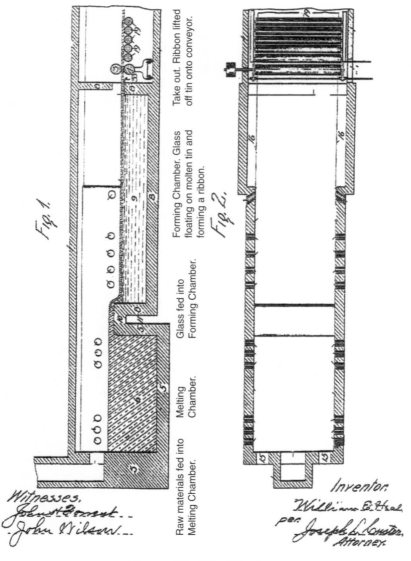

Patented Sept. 30, 1902.

W. E. HEAL.

MANUFACTURE OF WINDOW AND PLATE GLASS.

(Application filed Jan. 25, 1902.)

Fig. 1.

Fig. 2.

Take out. Ribbon lifted off tin onto conveyor.

Forming Chamber. Glass floating on molten tin and forming a ribbon.

Glass fed into Forming Chamber.

Melting Chamber.

Raw materials fed into Melting Chamber.

Witnesses.

Inventor.

per.

Attorney.

Figure 24   The Heal patent

Appendix 5   Biographies

Harry Pilkington, 1905–1983

Pilkington, William Henry (Harry), Baron Pilkington, manufacturer was born at Eccleston Grange on the western outskirts of St Helens, Lancashire, on 19 April 1905, the eldest of three sons and two daughters of Richard Austin Pilkington (1871–1951), a descendant of the glassmaking family, and Hope (b 1876/7), daughter of Sir Herbert Cozens-Hardy. His father's twin brother, Henry William, died of pulmonary phthisis in December 1902, and the damp, heavily polluted atmosphere of the chemical and other works at St Helens also disagreed with Richard Austin. He fell desperately ill in 1907 and in a last desperate attempt to save his life he was sent to live at Colorado Springs where the air was particularly dry and thin. The family glass manufacturing company, which did not think much of his chances of recovery, brought in as his replacement his brother-in-law, Edward Herbert Cozens-Hardy (1873–1956), an outstanding electrical engineer and partner in the London electrical engineering consultants, O'Gorman and Cozens-Hardy. Harry Pilkington accompanied his parents to Colorado where his brother, Lawrence Herbert Austin, was born in 1911. Austin Pilkington made a complete recovery, returned to St Helens in 1914, was able to serve with the south Lancashire battalion in the First World War, and became chairman of Pilkingtons on the unexpected death of Arthur Richard Pilkington (1871–1921). He proved a chairman who was reluctant to delegate responsibility and spent time during working days on interests, particularly education, outside the office. His younger brother, Alfred Cecil Pilkington (1875–1966), who was in charge of the technical side of the business, failed in his attempts to develop a continuous method of sheet glass manufacture capable of competing with those of Pilkingtons' competitors. The company nearly had to abandon sheet glass altogether but was saved by a third process, superior to the other two, the PPG process.

Pilkingtons' technically advanced plate glass factory kept the firm in profit, but the brothers, running the business as if it were still a partnership, did not invite confidence. Return on capital was disappointing and, after a small half-year loss was reported in March 1931, they had a disagreement. Both retired from active management. The opportunity had arrived, not before time, to begin to transform the management structure.

A trainee in the firm

Harry Pilkington entered the company as a family trainee straight from Cambridge in the summer of 1927, when the influence of the third generation led by his father and uncle – with William Norman Pilkington (1877–1935) and Guy Reginald Pilkington (1881–1970) – predominated over that of Cozens-Hardy and Geoffrey Langton Pilkington (1885–1972), an older fourth generation member who had arrived as a family trainee in 1909, distinguished himself in the war as an aviator, and returned to a directorship in 1919. While this board was showing poor results, the start of Harry Pilkington's academic career had proved no more promising. He was a shy boy and, so it is said, his father made no effort to build up his confidence. After an unremarkable schooling at Rugby he went up to Magdalene College, Cambridge, where he rowed for the college but showed no academic merit, obtaining a third-class degree in history (1925) and economics (1927). Two other fourth generation family trainees, sons of Pilkington daughters, joined at about the same time and also had to familiarise themselves with all parts of the business, and to be reported on by the managers concerned. Douglas Vandeleur Phelps (1904–1988), educated at Harrow School and Magdalene [sic] College, Oxford, where he read chemistry, arrived in 1927; Lancelot Roger Percival (1906–1964), who attended Eton College and Trinity College, Oxford, and was a distinguished athlete, arrived in the following year, when he also took part in the Olympic Games. Cozens-Hardy's son, Herbert Arthur (1907–1975), known as Peter, went to Pilkingtons as a trainee in 1932 after a spell with J. and J. Coleman, and

Lawrence Pilkington, Harry's brother, followed in 1935. The most remarkable fourth generation arrival, who was to be of particular help to Harry Pilkington, was Arthur Cope Pilkington (1909–1981). From Charterhouse School he went to the Royal Military College, Sandhurst, and spent five years as a regular officer in the Coldstream Guards. In 1934 he applied to join the company. He was a Roman Catholic and was allowed in (to quote the company minutes) only 'after various difficulties had been placed before him' and then only as a non-family trainee for a year in the first instance, it being made clear to him at the outset 'that the question of his religion will not prejudice his interests so long as it does not interfere with the business'. He did well and accordingly joined the family promotion contest in 1935. He was recalled to the guards during the Second World War, served in the guards armoured brigade, and was awarded an MC in 1945. He was appointed a Pilkington director in 1943 while away on active service.

The two resignations of 1931 gave Lord Cozens-Hardy (he inherited the barony in 1924 on the death of his elder brother) the chance to reorganise the company's top management. He created an executive committee, each person being responsible for a particular factory or function, under his chairmanship. His right-hand man was *Ronald Morce Weeks (1890–1960)*, manager of the highly successful plate glass factory. Weeks had joined the company in 1912 direct from Cambridge as a technical trainee, and distinguished himself in the First World War (DSO, MC and bar) before becoming plate glass works manager in 1921. In the reorganisation ten years later he was put in charge of all plate glass manufacture and technical services and was to succeed Cozens-Hardy as chairman of the executive committee in March 1939, but not for long. A leading territorial officer in the 1930s, he rose rapidly to become deputy chief of the Imperial General Staff. Chairmanship of the company itself passed to Geoffrey Pilkington after 1931.

The Cozens-Hardy regime discriminated against Harry Pilkington and the other family trainees by prolonging their traineeships, by bringing in non-family trainees, and by seeking out promising younger employees. Harry Pilkington and Douglas Phelps did not become directors until 1934 and Roger Percival not until 1936. Douglas Phelps later consolidated his position by marrying Cozens-Hardy's daughter, Helen Rosemary, in 1953. Two other family trainees did not make the grade at all. Raymond Pilkington left in 1936 after two years and William Lee Pilkington fared even worse: having joined in 1927 and been offered 'a final trial for a period of one year', he left to become a stockbroker. Harry Pilkington, on the other hand, soon had a lucky break. There were unexpected resignations on the sales side in 1935–6 and, soon after his thirtieth birthday, he found himself director in charge and was able to display a remarkable memory, head for figures, and appetite for long hours of work, travelling extensively and taking advantage of the newly developing air services to meet glass manufacturers and merchants as far away as Australia. In 1939, when the third generation had retired and members of the fourth went off to war, Harry Pilkington was left as second-in-command to Geoffrey Pilkington, who also became chairman of the executive committee on Weeks' departure from full-time management at St Helens. During the war the Pilkington factories at St Helens supplied all the glass needed by the blitzed cities (equivalent to the glazing of London twice over) and seized many continental producers' markets overseas.

Chairman of the company

After the war, Douglas Phelps succeeded Geoffrey Pilkington as chairman of the executive committee (1947) and Harry succeeded as chairman of the company (1949). Arthur Pilkington and Lawrence Pilkington became directors in 1943. The fourth generation, led by Harry Pilkington, had regained control of the business and, with one or two able men promoted from the higher levels of staff, they more than compensated for any shortcomings of their predecessors in the 1920s. Their achievement, however, would have been less considerable without another Pilkington, Alastair, who was not of the glassmaking family. His father, a businessman living in the south of England, keen on his family tree, had made contact with a Pilkington family shareholder with a similar interest. Having been unable to establish any link, the non-St Helens Pilkington revealed that his son, a former officer and prisoner of war, was at Cambridge completing his engineering degree, and would welcome the chance of a job at St Helens. So the future Sir Alastair Pilkington FRS, inventor of the float glass process, joined the fourth generation in August 1947 as a family trainee. That he obtained this remarkable privilege was thanks to the intelligent foresight and flexibility of Harry Pilkington and Douglas Phelps, who interviewed him in the first place.

After the war Pilkingtons became an international company in a much fuller sense. It had long participated in international associations of glass manufacturers, had attempted to make glass in other countries, and had participated in its manufacture in Australia and Argentina during the 1930s. It also processed its British glass into safety glass for the motor industry in several Commonwealth countries. In the later 1940s it went much further, establishing sheet glass factories in Canada and South Africa to safeguard its sales there. These international developments involved much new organisation at St Helens to supervise the planning and initial supply of foremen to train local workers. Throughout the world sales to its two main outlets, the motor and building industries, grew very quickly in response to the mid-1950s demand for glass. This was fortunate, for it was in 1955, when the company was extraordinarily profitable, that the momentous decision was taken to build a full-scale production plant for the entirely novel float process (basically pouring molten glass at 1000° C on to a bath of molten tin and floating the ribbon down a temperature gradient so that it could be taken off over rollers at 600° C). The promise of earlier experiments was not realised when the production plant came into use in May 1957, as the scientists in the research department had warned, and further development cost up to £1 million a year. Alastair Pilkington, a superb advocate, was able in person to plead his engineering team's case to the board; even so, further costly development would not have been sanctioned without the unflagging support of Sir Harry (who had been knighted in 1953). Success was publicly announced in January 1959, but it was not until 1962, and much further development, that the first licences were issued. After that, income increased as float glass replaced the more costly plate glass and in due course sheet glass as well. Technical ascendancy during Sir Harry's chairmanship gave the British company world leadership.

Sir Harry's chairmanship also saw the major restructuring of the business necessitated by its international growth. Divisional boards, subsidiary companies, and liaison committees were formed. In 1964 outside non-executive directors were introduced to the general board, all well known to Sir Harry, and in the following year he produced convincing arguments in the company's defence when it was investigated by the Monopolies Commission. He was created a life peer in 1968, saw the business launched as a public company in 1970, and handed over the chairmanship to Sir Alastair Pilkington in 1973. During his twenty-four-year chairmanship the capital employed in the business grew from £12.5 million to £206 million and sales to outside customers from £15.6 million to £177 million. The numbers employed went up from 15,233 to 31,200 and of these, those abroad increased from 667 to 9800.

Other activities and honours

As well as being actively concerned with the business at St Helens, Sir Harry also became involved in other matters, usually in London. He managed this by spending whole days in each place and travelling up and down between Liverpool and London by night sleeper. From 1944 to 1952 he chaired the

National Council of Building Material Producers and in May 1952 attracted attention in Whitehall by a report on the methods and costs of school building. A few months later the Pilkington board allowed him to accept the presidency of the Federation of British Industries (1953–5) on the grounds that it was not only an honour but also a national duty, but warned him against the further distracting invitations which would follow. He served on the important Crichel Down enquiry (1954) and chaired the royal commission on doctors' and dentists' remuneration (1957–60) and, immediately afterwards, the committee on broadcasting (1960–62), for which the Pilkington board gave permission only 'after considerable discussion'. He also served as a director of the Bank of England (1955–72) and on the Council of European Industrial Federations (1954–7). Like his father before him, he had an abiding interest in education which occupied more of his time as he grew older. He served as chairman of the National Advisory Council on Education for Industry and Commerce (1956–66) and was a member of the Manchester Business School's council (1964–72), president of the Association of Technical Institutions (1966–80), and first chancellor of Loughborough University of Technology (1966), and Kent (1968).

Religion, family and death

A lifelong Congregationalist, Sir Harry believed in the gospel of work and strict self-discipline, and rarely failed to attend chapel on Sunday morning. In business he believed in 'peace among the big manufacturers ... (which) can only be obtained by a spirit of mutual sacrifice and mutual trust'. His home remained on the outskirts of St Helens itself, in a house which the family had occupied since 1826. He was a keen rose grower and would some-times surprise his employees by turning up to prune their roses if his gardener was unable to do so. His devotion to the bicycle became legendary, particularly in the City. Much time in his last years was spent writing in his own hand to company pensioners who reached the age of eighty, and sometimes delivering these letters to their homes.

In 1930 Harry Pilkington married Rosamund Margaret (Penny) [*sic*; actually Peggy], daughter of Colonel Henry Davis Rowan of the Royal Army Medical Corps. They had a son and two daughters. His wife died of a heart attack in 1953 and his younger daughter was drowned in Iraq in 1960. In 1961 he married Mavis Joy Doreen, daughter of Gilbert Caffrey, cotton manufacturer, and former wife of John Hesketh Wilding, radiologist. Lord Pilkington died in St Helens on 22 December 1983, survived by his second wife.

Alastair Pilkington, 1905–1995

Alastair Pilkington, Glass Technologist, was born in Calcutta, India on 7 January 1920, the son of Colonel Lionel George Pilkington, an engineer born in Australia, and Evelyne Bethune, from a Scottish family with business interests in India. In 1923 the family returned to England, where Alastair (as he was known) went to Sherborne School. He was brought up in the Christian Science religion of his mother. He entered Trinity College, Cambridge in 1938.

It may be that two periods of his life were responsible for building in Alastair Pilkington a determination and intensity of purpose: Cambridge University and the Second World War. As a young undergraduate at Trinity he was a fine and extremely competent athlete, representing the university at squash, fives and tennis. He was the fives amateur champion of England and seldom lost a competitive game of squash.

He was called up in 1939, while at university, and served with the Royal Artillery. He was captured in Crete and spent three years as a prisoner of war. He spoke little of his experiences, but it is not hard to imagine that those three years contributed much to his great strength of character.

On 1 June 1945 he married Patricia Nicholls (d 1977), the daughter of Rear-Admiral Frank Elliott, with whom he had a daughter, Rosalind, and an adopted son, James.

He was chairman of Pilkington, the Merseyside glass manufacturers, from 1973 to 1980. Pilkington Brothers was founded at St Helens by Richard and William Pilkington in 1826; during Sir Alastair's career with the company, which he joined in 1947, he made an outstanding contribution to its growth and prosperity.

Although his surname was helpful, he was not, in fact, related to the St Helens Pilkingtons. This had become the dominant employer both in St Helens and in the British glass industry.

He was a remarkable man, whose life encompassed several careers; a scientist with management skills, a man of strong convictions passionately held and cogently argued.

He will be remembered primarily for his invention of the float process. Four years after joining Pilkington in 1947, he conceived the idea that molten glass could be formed into a continuous ribbon by pouring it into a bath of tin and 'floating' it while it cooled. In this way, neither surface would be marked by the rollers of the plate glass process or the glass distorted by the vertical pull of the sheet glass process.

Like the jet engine – a simple concept – but difficult to perfect. That it was perfected was due in large part to Alastair Pilkington's determination. He worked long hours with his team of scientists and glassmakers over seven years before understanding and then applying the pioneering physics, chemistry and engineering required to achieve success.

By 1976 twenty-one licensees were paying £20 million annually for the float process. By the end of the century cumulative licence revenue exceeded £600 million. The annual income from this source, however, fell to about £5 million a year by 2000.

Sir Alastair retired as chairman of Pilkington at the age of 60, several years earlier than was customary in those days, saying that, although he had greatly enjoyed his time at Pilkington, he looked forward to enjoying a second career while he was still active. This he achieved. Apart from skiing, paragliding and sailing, he took on the chairmanship of Chloride and served as a director of the Bank of England and a non-executive director of BP, British Rail and the Wellcome Foundation.

He contributed to his first love, the advancement of science and education, through his membership of the Science Advisory Committee for Science and Technology and the Science Research Council. He was president of the British Association between 1983 and 1984 and vice-president of its Foundation of Science and Technology in 1986. He was elected a Fellow of the Royal Society in 1969, knighted in 1970, and received doctorates and fellowships from 13 academic institutions, as well as numerous scientific awards.

Alastair Pilkington also played an important part in community life. He was closely involved in the creation of the first enterprise agency in the UK – the Community of St Helens Trust – from which grew Business in the Community, of which he was the founder chairman.

In 1990 he took on the task of raising money for his university by becoming chairman of the Cambridge Foundation. He was for ten years Pro-Chancellor of Lancaster University and was elected Chancellor of Liverpool University.

Alastair Pilkington will be remembered personally for his unfailing kindness, his concern for others, his enquiring mind and the stimulation of his company. He achieved his objective of a second career, but it was his character to achieve what he set out to do.

(Dictionary of National Biography)

Appendix 6   Obituaries

'Stay-at-home' Richard (Richard Pilkington, 1795–1869)

It becomes our painful duty to chronicle the death of this esteemed gentleman, which occurred at Windle Hall, at half-past four o'clock on Thursday morning. He had not been in his usual health for a considerable time, but it was only a fortnight before his decease that he was actually confined to his residence, and unable to appear in public. Few will hear of his demise without the most sincere sorrow. Born in St Helens, springing from a family long and honourably identified with the district, and contributing, in no inconsiderable degree, to the prosperity which we happily see around us, Mr Pilkington was naturally universally known and as universally respected; but beyond these recommendations to the public esteem, he was endowed with a generous heart, and a manly and consistent character. He sat on the magisterial bench about twenty years, and was always known as one of the most painstaking, attentive and humane administrator of the law in the county. From his childhood the lamented gentleman was a member of the Independent community, and was the best known of all the friends and frequenters of the old chapel in which his father worshipped before his birth. A Liberal in politics, he was the staunch friend of the party of his choice. He never veered from the straight course in his political life – his principles being as fixed as his career was upright. Though exceedingly popular, he was naturally of a reserved and retiring character; and he invariably, whenever business arrangements permitted, loved to go back to the quiet and seclusion of his family circle, in the midst of whom his soul passed calmly away.

'Go-getter' William (William Pilkington, 1800–1872)

Last Saturday we fulfilled the melancholy duty of recording briefly the death of this much-esteemed gentleman, which took place on Thursday afternoon, the 12th instant, at his residence, Downing Hall, Holywell, at the ripe age of 72 years. We now present our readers with a succinct memoir of his career – which time did not admit of last week – because so prominent a citizen should not be allowed to pass away from amongst us with anything like an ordinary obituary notice. His death severs one of the few links which bind the present with the past of St Helens, and removes the last surviving representative of the energetic men who constructed the cradle of the prosperity of the town. The old and new orders of things were personified in him: he had seen the light in the one and helped to create the other. He passed the years of youth in a then picturesque village; in early manhood he essayed successfully to create a manufacturing industry by which he hoped to spread additional prosperity on the place of his birth; and in middle and old age he toiled with all the vigour of his nature in the midst of a commercial life that surpassed the most sanguine dream of his incipient maturity. His early associates and fellow-labourers are all, we believe, gone the way of mortality, and he survived long enough to cast an immortelle on the grave of the last of them – his venerated brother, Richard, who was laid to rest more than two years ago.

At this time we find his giving indications of his speculative nature, in his connections with various business projects; but the great step of his commercial life was that which carried him into the glass trade, and led by successive stages to the vast establishment which is now held by the family. It was a bold venture to manufacture crown glass in St Helens, and a company was formed to carry out the project. The works were promoted by Mr P Greenall, Mr T Bell, Mr W Bell, Mr J Bromilow, and Mr John Barnes, and to their names that of Mr William Pilkington was added. They were commenced in 1827, and remained some time under the management of Mr Wm Bell, and Mr James Bromilow, partially assisted by Mr W Pilkington. This continued until Mr Pilkington, purchasing the interest of all the partners, except Mr Greenall, entered on the sole management on 1st January 1829, and continued it alone for seven and a half years, leaving Mr Richard Pilkington to conduct the wine and spirit distillery in Church Street, until that firm of Pilkington and Sons was disposed of to Messrs Webster and Sons, the present possessors. Mr Richard Pilkington joined his brother at the glassworks in September 1836. They subsequently purchased Mr Peter Greenall's share, and though retaining the style and title of St Helens Crown Glass Co., yet the only partners were Wm and Richard Pilkington, until it became, as it is now, Pilkington Bros, by the admission of their sons. The cone which still stands in the midst, so to say, of the works, marks the first effort of the firm, in the to them new trade, and there was no exertion wanting on their part to make it successful. But the concern did not prosper. Either through some fault in the construction or the way-wardness of the workmen but generally supposed the latter, the products were not all saleable, nor even a reasonable proportion of them. To add to their difficulties the duty then paid on glass was most oppressive. Insomuch as the excise claimed an impost, not alone on the glass sold, but on the glass as it was manufac-tured, unsold and unsaleable articles were taxed until at one time Mr Pilkington stated himself that upward of £16,000 worth lay in store which was not likely to be purchased, but which had been taxed every ounce. This was a critical juncture, and it looked as if the doors must be closed. The repeal of the tax was a benefit which was immediately and favourably felt. We understand that the progress of the works was nevertheless hampered by inefficient management, and Mr Pilkington, in a lucky moment gave the direction of the mechanical department to a workman named James Kenmore, who still lives, and is highly respected by the present proprietors. He was disinclined to assume the respon-sibility, but his scruples were overborne, and prosperity dawned under his sound practical administration. Extension followed extension as the orders outgrew the resources; and furnaces sprang up around the comparatively venerable cone. With a view to retrain the destructive waywardness of the workmen which entailed constant and severe losses upon the firm, Mr William had a room fitted up at the works in which he frequently passed the entire night, and from which he would at any moment emerge and walk through the various departments of the works. His watchfulness in this respect had the desired effect, and was after a time unnecessary. We need not trace the history of the works any further. All who know St Helens know that under the fostering care of their owners, and especially the sleepless energy of Mr William, they gradually became what they are today, a splendid monument of well-directed intelligence and business aptitude.

Turning from his manufacturing career, we find that Mr Pilkington's excellent qualities were recognised outside the sphere of business. About twenty-six years ago he was appointed to the commission of the peace for the county of Lancashire, and some time afterwards appointed a deputy-lieutenant. The honour of the magistracy was a testimony to his character and position; but the other office was of a still rarer and more exalted character, and is a striking evidence of the high esteem in which he was held. He took an interest in the well-being of the late Mechanics' Institute as he did in everything that could benefit the working classes, and he presided frequently at the Saturday evening entertainment. He was chairman of the time-honoured St Helens Book Club, and presided for many years at its annual meetings. When his family began to gather round him, he left Church Street, removing to Millbrook House, where he lived for several years and then took up his residence at Eccleston Hall. After a residence there of nearly twenty years, he determined, under the irresistible influence of failing health, to leave this insalubrious neighbourhood, and retire to live at Downing Hall, the ancient seat of the Pennants, and now the property of the Earl of Denbigh.

Few men pass away from early labour leaving a memory on which no one can consistently cast an aspersion. Fewer still fail to be pursued to the very grave with envenomed shafts of hostile criticism. It will therefore be a source of worthy pride to Mr

Pilkington's living relatives and descendants to know that no slur can be cast upon his memory. 'Full of years, and full of honours' he journeyed to his final home; and his townsmen every one mourn his demise. He earned respect as an employer of labour with whom probity was the line of life. His workmen honoured him as one who recognised how essential they were to the industrial machine, and studied their wants as he would his own. The great glassworks were not merely a place in which men could toil, and coin the gold which enriched themselves, their employers, and the community – but a nursery of useful recreative and educational institutions, in which the wearied mechanic might find pleasure and relaxation. He had not to seek for it elsewhere – in the music hall or the gin palace – it was provided on the spot where his avocations bound him, and it was his own fault if he ignored it. As a magistrate he made a special reputation. Gifted with clear-sightedness, which was sharpened by his active business life, he was singularly prompt in his decisions, and seldom erred in his estimate of character. Those who had to come before him in this judicial capacity found him upright and unswerving in his sense of justice.

We are loath to give this sketch the slightest political cast, but it would be unjust to so prominent a citizen to omit this particular feature of his character. He had an aversion to the heat of party strife, and consistently avoided it, content with giving the weight of his mature wisdom and the influence of his personal convictions, to the cause which he had at heart. His removal to Holywell left a blank in the circles which knew him most, and his eternal transfer to another world seems more than a domestic bereavement. He was 'every inch a gentleman', one of Nature's own creation – a title which no potentate, however despotic, can either confer or abrogate.

(*The St Helens Newspaper*, September 1872)